"Treat the earth well.

It was not given to you by your parents.

It was loaned to you by your children."

NATIVE AMERICAN PROVERB

WILL THE FLOWER SLIP THROUGH THE ASPHALT

Writers Respond to

Capitalist Climate Change

Naomi Klein

Carlos Drummond de Andrade

John Bellamy Foster

Ghassan Hage

Rafia Zakaria

Masturah Alatas

Shalini Singh

susan abulhawa

WITH AN AFTERWORD BY Amitav Ghosh

EDITED BY Vijay Prashad

WILL THE FLOWER SLIP THROUGH THE ASPHALT

LeftWord

Published in February 2017 by
LeftWord Books
2254/2A Shadi Khampur
New Ranjit Nagar
New Delhi 110008
INDIA

LeftWord Books is the publishing division of
Naya Rasta Publishers Pvt. Ltd.

leftword.com

ISBN 978-93-80118-47-5

'Let Them Drown: The Violence of Othering in a Warming World' by
Naomi Klein was first delivered as the 2016 Edward W. Said London
Lecture and subsequently published in the *London Review of Books*, June
2016. It republished here with the author's permission, with some modest
edits.

'What Nutmeg Can Tell Us About Globalization' by Amitav Ghosh.
Copyright ©Amitav Ghosh 2016, used by permission of The Wylie
Agency (UK) Limited.

Printed and bound by Chaman Enterprises, Delhi

This book is dedicated to

the defenders of the earth and its people,

specifically to two who have been killed

as they stood between the

Future and the Past:

BERTA CÁCERES (1972-2016)

of the Council of Popular and Indigenous

Organisations of Honduras

ISIDRO BALDENEGRO LÓPEZ (1966-2017)

of the Tarahumara community

Contents

Contents

CARLOS DRUMMOND DE ANDRADE

A Flor e a Náusea

Imprisoned by my class and my clothes
I go in white through the gray street.
Melancholy men, shopkeepers peer at me.
Should I continue until I sicken?
Can I revolt without arms?

Dirty eyes on the clock tower:
No, the time has not come for complete justice.
It is still the time of feces, bad poems, hallucinations and
waiting.

The poor time, the poor poet
Stuck in the same impasse.

In vain I try to explain myself, but the walls are deaf.
Under the skin of words there are ciphers and codes.
The sun consoles the sick, but does not renew them.
Things. How sad are things, considered out of context.
A flower bloomed in the street!

They'll vomit this tedium across the city.
Forty years and not a single problem
resolved, not even close.

Not a single letter written nor received.
All the men return home.
They are less free but they carry newspapers
and decipher the world, knowing that they've lost it.

Crimes of the earth, how does it forgive them?
I took part in many, others I hid.
Some I thought were beautiful, they were published.
Gentle crimes, that helped me live.
The daily ration of error, distributed at home.
The feral bakers of evil.
The feral milkmen of evil.

Set it all aflame, including myself.
To the boy of 1918, they called an anarchist.
But my hate is the best part of me.
With it I save myself
And give a little hope to a few.

Far away they pass by, trams, buses,
Rivers of steel traffic.
A flower, though faded
Evades the police, breaks the asphalt.
Be completely silent, stop your business
I swear a flower grew.
Its color is unnoticed.
Its petals aren't open.
Its name is not in the books
It is ugly. But it is truly a flower.

I sit on the ground of the country's
Capital at five in the afternoon
And slowly pass my hand over this fraile thing.
Beside the mountains, dense clouds swell.
Little white points dance on the surface of the sea,
Chickens run in panic.

It is ugly. But it is a flower.
It slipped through the asphalt, the boredom, the disgust
and the hate.

From *A Rosa do Povo* (1945).

VIJAY PRASHAD

Introduction

Isn't our life a tunnel between two clarities?
Pablo Neruda, *Libros de las pregutas*, 1974

In his final press conference as Secretary-General of the
United Nations in December 2016, Ban Ki-moon turned
his attention to climate change. 'The Paris Agreement on
climate change is a precious achievement that we must
support and nurture', he said. 'There is no turning back.'

Secretary Ban's comment — *there is no turning back*
— was pointed. It comes in the context of the rise to
political office of a number of 'climate sceptics', political
leaders who believe either that global climate change
is not occurring or who believe that there is little that
humans can do to reverse these changes. Such political
leaders — people like Donald Trump of the United States
— would like to set aside the 2016 Paris Agreement
on climate change. Erik Solheim, the head of the UN
Environmental Programme, indicated his concern that
'some elite American politicians deny science. You will
be in the Middle Ages if you deny science.'

Denial of climate science is only the symptom of a
much deeper problem that confronts the planet. It is the
endemic crisis-ridden capitalism that lashes about like an

injured dragon, breathing fire here and whipping its tail over there. Fatally wounded, capitalism seeks regeneration through any means — whether by the seizure of precious natural resources or the cannibalization of human labour. Whether it is talk of 'sustainable development' or 'carbon-based development', the common factor here is to increase growth rates by greater exploitation of nature and humanity. The various reports of the UN's Intergovernmental Panel on Climate Change show that human life cannot be sustained if the growth trajectory continues along the path set by capitalism. There is a powerful contradiction between the needs of a parasitic capitalism and its natural and human host. Both cannot survive. One will have to vanquish the other.

The idea that capitalism has no respect for nature and the habitat of our planet has been clear for generations. In a moving letter to her friend Sophie Liebknecht, Rosa Luxemburg wrote on 2 May 1917,

Yesterday I was reading about the reasons for the disappearance of songbirds in Germany. The spread of scientific forestry, horticulture, and agriculture, have cut them off from their nesting places and their food supply. More and more, with modern methods, we are doing away with hollow trees, wastelands, brushwood, fallen leaves. I felt sore at heart. I was not thinking so much about the loss of pleasure for human beings, but I was so much distressed at the idea of the stealthy and inexorable destruction of these defenceless little creatures, that the tears came into my eyes. I was reminded of a book I read in Zurich, in which Professor Sieber describes the dying-out of the Redskins in North America. Just like the birds, they have been gradually driven from their hunting grounds by civilized men.

The Russian Revolution had broken out a few months previously. Tensions in Germany had alerted Luxemburg and her comrades to the possibility of an uprising in the heart of Europe. Luxemburg was in prison, from where she wrote this letter. Why was this revolutionary — steeped in the ethos of revolutionary change at the time of great anticipation — writing about songbirds? Not because, she told her friend, 'like so many spiritually bankrupt politicians, I seek refuge and find repose in nature. Far from it, in nature at every turn I see so much cruelty that I suffer greatly.' The intimate linkage between capitalism's disdain for the natural world and its scorn for the working-class seemed apparent to Luxemburg. Her ethic was not to bemoan the demise of nature because it would hinder human consumption of the natural world. She was upset by the death of the songbirds because of the necessary linkage in capitalist history between the eradication of nature and the genocide of humans. This was not *human nature* at work, but the system of capitalism that required nature and humans as resources for the ceaseless profit motive.

Luxemburg's assessment of capitalism — *The Accumulation of Capital* (1913) — had made the case for capital's relentless search for new investment opportunities, vanquishing all barriers, devouring all resources. Her letter to Liebknecht should be read in light of Luxemburg's argument about how capitalism seeks to colonize the non-capitalist environment, and without this terrain it would collapse onto itself. This is what Marx meant when he wrote in *Capital*, vol. 3, that the 'limit of capital is capital itself'. Without this permanent ravaging of natural and human resources, capital cannot function. When human misery or social inequality and when climate change become limits, they have to be set aside. The attack on basic liberal concern for the poor (demonstrated through welfare payments and humanitarian aid) and the attack on climate science are of a piece — they are essentially attempts to conduct ideological war on the cultural barriers to untrammelled capitalism as preparation for the destruction of the natural and human habitat. Capitalism developed, Marx wrote in *Capital*, out of the 'discovery of gold and silver in America, the extirpation, enslavement entombment in mines of the aboriginal population, the beginning of the conquest and looting of the East Indies, the turning of Africa into a warren for the commercial looting of black-skins.' This is what Marx called originary or 'primitive' accumulation (*ursprüngliche akkumulation*). It would reappear each time capitalism ran into a crisis — the eternal return of brutal accumulation on a global-scale. Marx and Luxemburg produced thunderous prose to denounce the destruction of nature and the humans who had been othered. This was their jeremiad against 'civilization'.

In his new book — *The Great Derangement:*

Climate Change and the Unthinkable (2016) — Amitav Ghosh rightly points out that capitalism alone is not the 'principal fault line on the landscape of climate change'. He says that there are 'two interconnected but equally important rifts', namely capitalism and imperialism. Ghosh describes imperialism — or empire, as he calls it — as 'an aspiration to dominance on the part of some of the most powerful structures of the world's most powerful states'. Marx and Luxemburg, like Ghosh, saw imperialism as inherent in capitalism, that the ravaging of the planet for the sake of interests rooted in Europe (and later the United States) was essential to the system. Merchants and markets elsewhere had to be subordinated to the will of the 'most powerful states'. The people in these 'most powerful states' saw an expansion in their consumption patterns far in excess of the people of the rest of the planet. No wonder, then, that while the US population is not more than five per cent of the world's population, it consumes a quarter of the world's energy. Stunningly, the poorest ten per cent of the world's population consumed merely 0.5% of the share of the world's private consumption, while the wealthiest one per cent consumed fifty-nine per cent of that pie. If the poorest consumed like the richest, we would need several planets to sustain ourselves. It is because of this disparity of lifestyle and power that the Global North imagines that one solution to the crisis is what Christian Parenti called 'the politics of the armed lifeboat'. Endless counter-insurgency combined with seizure of resources by force and militarized borders provides the basis for the 'armed lifeboat'. Ghosh suggests that this is an utopian solution. 'We are in an era', he writes, 'when the body of the nation can no longer be conceived of as consisting only of a territorialized human population: its very sinews are now revealed to be intertwined with forces that cannot be confined by boundaries.' This is precisely the argument, and tone, of Ghosh's afterword for this book. Imperialism — or empire — projects its own fantasy solution to the crisis, which are fiercer wars and higher borders. What will the gunships do when the waters rise?

Liberals blush at the prospect of the politics of the armed lifeboat. They would like a less aggressive solution, which — typically — they find in technology. The name for this is 'Green Capitalism'. A generation after Luxemburg, in 1950, Joseph Schumpeter — an Austrian Finance Minister in 1919 and Harvard University Professor — looked carefully at the dynamic of capitalism and worried that it would collapse because its own 'creative success' had pushed it to its limits. Competition between firms leads to the production of massive amounts of goods (overproduction), which cannot be purchased by workers whose wages either decline or remain flat (underconsumption). Firms go out of business and capitalism enters a phase of stagnation. It is only technological breakthroughs of one kind or another that enable capitalism to re-emerge with great dynamism. Schumpeter called this 'creative destruction', annotating what Marx had noted in his *Grundrisse*, that capitalism contains an 'endless and limitless drive to go beyond its limiting barrier. Every limit appears as a barrier to be overcome.' Schumpeter did not share the tone of denunciation that was common to Marx and Luxemburg. His was a bloodless prose, hopeful in the capacity of civilization to prevail over its worst instincts. On this, Schumpeter was wrong. Technological change, for Schumpeter, would save capitalism from its inherent problems but such changes increase reliance on machines, create unemployment and disturb the equilibrium of production and consumption. Talk of 'green capitalism' is along this grain. It is not that new technologies — wind turbines, solar panels — will not be valuable, it is that capitalism as a social system will be unable to transform itself from the needs of profit to the needs of society. For example, the massive investment needed to change the energy systems from fossil-fuels to green-energy would hamper profit and encroach on private property rights and private investments. And further, the reliance on machines and the creation of unemployment — in labour heavy sectors such as mining — could only be offset by a new understanding of employment (a socialist understanding by which people are paid to live, not forced to starve) where ideas of a Six Hour Day and a Guaranteed National Income are central to the discussion. Without a direct challenge to capitalist profit and the idea of ceaseless growth, no such major and essential transformation is possible. Instead, what we find is that nuclear energy — highly profitable thanks to massive subsidies — and 'clean coal' are smuggled in as 'green energy'.

Naomi Klein's *This Changes Everything* (2014) has a subtitle that puts the point bluntly and quite perfectly: *Capitalism vs. The Climate*. Either capitalism is allowed to continue its devastating dynamic or the climate, namely the natural and human habitat, will be able to survive. There are, Klein argues, no capitalist solutions to the climate problem. Nor are there capitalist solutions to the problem of human inequality and under-development. In 1979, Raúl Prebsich, the first secretary general of the UN Conference on Trade and Development (UNCTAD), remarked that 'we thought that an acceleration of the rate of growth would solve all problems. This was our great mistake.' Only the demographically insignificant 'privileged consumption society', he said, benefits from the growth. Development plans that were authorized by the Global North resisted 'changes in the social structure', Prebisch said mournfully, while what was truly need was a 'complete social transformation'. Klein emphatically says that for the climate to be saved, capitalism must be overcome,

> Our economy is at war with many forms of life on earth, including human life. What the climate needs to avoid collapse is a contraction in humanity's use of resources; what our economic model demands to avoid collapse is unfettered expansion. Only one of these sets of rules can be changed, and it's not the laws of nature.

There are two clarities — that of capitalism and that of climate. They produce different realities, says Naomi

Klein: one malevolent and the other benevolent. The choice is stark, which is why she poses it as a question. There is no nuance here. Nuance will not help the people of the South Pacific. They are drowning in capitalism's surge.

CANARIES IN THE SOUTH PACIFIC

Sitting in the United Nations General Assembly chamber to listen to the president of Kiribati at the opening of the UN session is always a sobering experience. The presidents — Teburoro Tito, Anote Tong and Taneti Mamau — have been spokespersons for the islands and island cultures that totter on the edge of extinction as a result of climate change. 'Already we have whole villages being washed away', Tong said in 2012. 'There's no running away from that reality.' Over a decade before he made these comments, the islands of Abanuea and Tebua Tarawa vanished under the waters. The island of Tepuka Savilivili lost its coconut trees due to salination. Kiribati, located in the centre of the Pacific Ocean, takes its name for a certain pronunciation of the last name of Captain Thomas Gilbert. On the way to China after having dropped off a boatload of convicts at Botany Bay in 1788, Gilbert chanced on these islands. They took his name. One of them had an earlier name, Abanuea, which means *the beach which is long-lasting*. It lasted a long time, but could not withstand the rising ocean in 1999. That's when it went under. The Gilbertese lost two islands that year. Others have since followed. Five of the Solomon Islands (Kale, Rapita, Rehana, Kakatina and Zollies) vanished in the past decades. They are all climate victims.

The fate of the small island is to disappear.

Abanuea, the island with beaches that were fated for forever, was the canary. No wonder that President Tong lived with his nightmares. 'For some time I did not sleep because I didn't have a solution to a problem that there wasn't a solution to. What happens to us in the future? Do we disappear as a culture?'

In May 2012, at the UN's Economic and Social Commission of Asia and the Pacific (ESCAP), Pacific Island nations came to talk about climate change and their cruel fate. Kiribati's Finance and Economic Development Minister Tom Murdoch announced that his small island state has established the largest marine protected area in the Ocean — the Phoenix Islands Protected Area, which is more than 400,000 sq. kms, or 11% of Kiribati's Exclusive Economic Zone. 'The Ocean is fundamental to our cultural identity', Murdoch said, 'Our green economy is very *blue*. It has been said that we are not a small island developing country but rather a large ocean developing economy. We are trying to do our part in the sustainable management of our ocean and marine environment.' The language of sustainable development whipped around the ESCAP discussion. No-one had the courage to say that the system was fundamentally committed to detrimental climate change, and that only a transformation of the system would save the small islands. The voters rejected Murdoch in 2015.

People want something more powerful than the idea of 'sustainable development'. It is empty of content. They want a new compact, a new way to live and to organize our social and natural wealth.

Tuvalu's Minister of Trade Lotoala Metia told his fellow officials that his country is trying to move from fossil fuels, on which the island is totally dependent, to renewable energy by 2020. There is something obscene about these pledges coming from countries that barely contribute to the climatic shifts. Out of the 186 countries that reported figures for greenhouse gas emissions, Kiribati came in at 185. The three biggest emitters are the USA, European Union and China. It is worth recollecting that at the 2011 Durban meeting, the major environmental NGOs wrote to US Secretary of State Hillary Clinton pointing out that the US was the 'major obstacle' to any progress in global talks. Even the European Union openly criticized the US for 'overlooking the facts' of climate disturbances. This was when US liberalism was in charge. Now Donald Trump is the president. He rejects the idea of climate mitigation. Will his Secretary of State — the oil magnate Rex Tillerson — be worse than Clinton? Will he want to sign a climate treaty with a drilling bit instead of a pen?

Behind the scenes of that Durban meeting, as one of the Wikileaks tranches demonstrates, the US colluded with the Europeans to scuttle any attempt by the UN and by the BASIC (Brazil, South Africa, India, and China) countries to create an effective climate treaty. Despite the public declarations on behalf of climate legislation by

President Barack Obama, his administration used every
dirty trick, including withholding aid, to secure votes
against effective climate legislation at Copenhagen and
Durban. Michael Froman, US deputy national security
advisor, wanted to deny the BASIC states a victory not
only for climate negotiations but also to break their
political momentum. 'It is remarkable how closely co-
ordinated the BASIC group has become in international
fora', Froman wrote from Brussels, 'taking turns to
impede US/EU initiatives and playing the US and EU
off against each other. BASIC countries have widely
differing interests, but have subordinated these to their
common short-term goals. The US and EU need to learn
from this co-ordination and work much more closely
and effectively together ourselves, to better handle third
country obstructionism and avoid future train wrecks
on climate, Doha or financial regulatory reform.'

The newly confident Global South did not roll
over. The largest states, the BASIC countries, stood
by their own view that any cut back on carbon would
have to come with technological transfers and financial
assistance to facilitate 'leap frogging' over a carbon
modernity towards a non-carbon civilization. Even this
is a tepid programme. The BASIC countries are reliant
upon carbon-development, pillaging the planet in the
name of poverty eradication but actually benefitting
very small minorities of the über-rich. But even this
limited demand by the BASIC countries could not be
accepted by the North. It would rather try to use its
minuscule foreign aid program to break the coalitions

of the Global South. In 2010, the Danish Ambassador to Bolivia told the US chargé in La Paz, 'Danish Prime Minister [Anders Fogh] Rasmussen spent an unpleasant 30 minutes with [Bolivian President Evo] Morales, during which Morales thanked him for [$30m a year in] bilateral aid, but refused to engage on climate change issues. The Danes said they are "fed up" with Bolivia and the ALBA [Bolivarian Alliance for the Peoples of Our America] countries, who continue to mount legal and propaganda arguments against the Copenhagen Accord, but that they will continue to consult with their European Union partners on ways to influence the [Bolivian Government's] position.' No such luck. Morales remained obdurate. The North must cut its high per-capital fossil fuel emissions and provide a fund for the South to move to renewable energy. In terms of energy use per capita, the top five users are the United States, Russia, France, Germany and Japan. Energy use per capita in the countries of the Global South is a fraction of what one sees in the North. Morales picked the sore that the Northern bureaucrats wanted to keep covered over.

Dr. Kosi Latu, a leader of the small island states, complains about the direction of the climate debate, and joined President Tong in his despondency. 'For us in the Pacific, it's more than [poverty reduction and green technology]. I'm talking about the survival of our peoples in the sense that due to climate change impacts, we stand to lose our land, our histories and cultures, our nationalities.' Writing this down in my notebook, I wondered in the margin whether there would be anyone paying attention to this aspect of the demise of the small islands — the death of cultures that have been developed over thousands of years. When the island vanishes, the material basis of the culture of its people will also go. Those who survive will become 'climate refugees', a term that the UN is trying to establish. They will move to New Zealand or even Zambia (whose late president welcomed the I-Kiribati) — although New Zealand has fought tooth and nail to refuse to allow Ioane Teitiota to become the first 'climate change refugee' (he was deported to Kiribati in 2016). Since most 'climate change refugees' are already 'othered, living — as Naomi Klein put it — in 'fossil fuel sacrificial zones', who cares about the Nigerian coastal communities or the Mi'kmaq island communities?

Lives will alter. The basis of the I-Kiribati will shift. There is nothing wrong with that in essence. Culture is not eternal — social forms from elsewhere transact into our lives, and if these enrich our cultural world in some way they stick. But what is to take place to the I-Kiribatis and their fellows is not the essence of normal cultural interchange — after all the I-Kiribatis take their own name from Thomas Gilbert and are not averse to cultural transactions (former President Tong's family came to the island from China after World War 2). What is at issue is the forewarned but cataclysmic annihilation of the social basis of I-Kiribati cultural life — an annihilation that is comparable to the cultural genocide visited upon the Native Americans by the Colombian crossing.

Is there a future of the 'sea of islands'? Not if the carbon civilization continues its pace onward. The rising seas will reclaim our ground, sings the I-Kiribati poet Jane Resture in 1999 as Abanuea sinks under the sea,

> While far away they pour their fumes into the clear blue sky
> not knowing and never caring why
> the world is beginning to die.

IMAGINE THE END OF CAPITALISM, THE FUTURE OF THE PLANET

In 2016, Naomi Klein delivered the Edward Said lecture in London. The lecture linked two major themes — the question of climate and the question of occupation (with Palestine as the focus). In a wide-ranging and deeply humane lecture, Klein pointed out that those who are 'othered' will be the first victims of the climate catastrophe. When I heard her lecture I thought immediately about the people of the small islands and the low coastlines who have already been vanquished by the current mode of production. This volume collects not only Naomi Klein's superb essay, but also reactions from important writers who live across the globe and who write about places as diverse as Malaysia and North America. Their reflections are sometimes direct notes on Klein's lecture — as with the essays by John Bellamy Foster and by Ghassan Hage. They are sometimes meditations that are spurred by Klein's insights — Rafia Zakaria takes us to the shoreline of Karachi, Masturah Alatas wonders about hijab and air-conditioning in Malaysia, Shalini Singh meanders through the climate wars in India, and susan abulhawa writes from the 'fossil fuel sacrifice zone' at Standing Rock (North Dakota, USA). The book closes with Amitav Ghosh's meditation on nutmeg and cloves, leading to important insights into globalization, interconnectedness and transformation.

The book opens with a poem by the Brazilian writer Carlos Drummond de Andrade (1902-1987), which was read out by the Brazilian actor Fernanda Montenegro (in Portuguese) and by the English actor Judi Dench (in English) at the 2016 Olympics. The image of the flower piercing the asphalt gives this book its title. When I first read this poem I thought of the coal fires in Jharia in India's eastern state of Jharkhand. These fires, inside the coalmines, broke out in 1916 and have burned for a century. Not only do they spew carbon into the atmosphere, but they heat the ground on which the miners — many children, mostly tribal — walk on their way into the smoky caverns. For a hundred years the government has done nothing to stop the fire, to prevent the colourful plumes of smoke from blowing out of the earth — the only flowers that one can see in the area. This is not the flower that the poet aches to see break through the asphalt.

Please read these essays as talismans against climate catastrophe, as an attempt to conjure flowers to break through the asphalt. Treat them as an invitation to write your own talismans, condensed magical powers

27

to get us all onto the streets to demand not 'sustainable development' but something more — a new world, a new system, a new compact between humans and nature, between human economic systems and human social dreams. In 2003, the literary critic Fredric Jameson wrote, 'Someone once said that it is easier to imagine the end of the world than to imagine the end of capitalism' (Jameson was most likely channelling the novelist J. G. Ballard). In our time, this is perfectly true. Novels and films, television shows and memes are more likely to acknowledge the destruction of the planet through climate change than to portray a future world free of the system of capitalism. Our task as writers is to help people imagine the end of capitalism before the end of the planet. It should be an easy choice.

NAOMI KLEIN

Let Them Drown

The Violence of Othering in a Warming World

Edward Said was no tree-hugger. Descended from traders, artisans and professionals, he once described himself as 'an extreme case of an urban Palestinian whose relationship to the land is basically metaphorical'. In *After the Last Sky*, his meditation on the photographs of Jean Mohr, he explored the most intimate aspects of Palestinian lives, from hospitality to sports to home décor. The tiniest detail — the placing of a picture frame, the defiant posture of a child — provoked a torrent of insight from Said. Yet when confronted with images of Palestinian farmers — tending their flocks, working the fields — the specificity suddenly evaporated. Which crops were being cultivated? What was the state of the soil? The availability of water? Nothing was forthcoming. 'I continue to perceive a population of poor, suffering, occasionally colourful peasants, unchanging and collective', Said confessed. This perception was 'mythic', he acknowledged — yet it remained.

If farming was another world for Said, those

29

Naomi Klein

who devoted their lives to matters like air and water pollution appear to have inhabited another planet. Speaking to his colleague Rob Nixon, he once described environmentalism as 'the indulgence of spoiled tree-huggers who lack a proper cause'. But the environmental challenges of the Middle East are impossible to ignore for anyone immersed, as Said was, in its geopolitics. This is a region intensely vulnerable to heat and water stress, to sea-level rise and to desertification. A recent paper in *Nature Climate Change* predicts that, unless we radically lower emissions and lower them fast, large parts of the Middle East will likely 'experience temperature levels that are intolerable to humans' by the end of this century. And that's about as blunt as climate scientists get. Yet environmental issues in the region still tend to be treated as afterthoughts, or luxury causes. The reason is not ignorance, or indifference. It's just bandwidth. Climate change is a grave threat but the most frightening impacts are in the medium term. And in the short term, there are always far more pressing threats to contend with: military occupation, air assault, systemic discrimination, embargo. Nothing can compete with that — nor should it attempt to try.

There are other reasons why environmentalism might have looked like a bourgeois playground to Said. The Israeli state has long coated its nation-building project in a green veneer — it was a key part of the Zionist 'back to the land' pioneer ethos. And in this context trees, specifically, have been among the most potent weapons of land grabbing and occupation. It's not only

30

the countless olive and pistachio trees that have been uprooted to make way for settlements and Israeli-only roads. It's also the sprawling pine and eucalyptus forests that have been planted over those orchards, as well as over Palestinian villages, most notoriously by the Jewish National Fund (JNF), which, under its slogan 'Turning the Desert Green', boasts of having planted 250 million trees in Israel since 1901, many of them non-native to the region. In publicity materials, the JNF bills itself as just another green NGO, concerned with forest and water management, parks and recreation. It also happens to be the largest private landowner in the state of Israel, and despite a number of complicated legal challenges, it still refuses to lease or sell land to non-Jews.

I grew up in a Jewish community where every occasion — births and deaths, Mother's Day, bar mitzvahs — was marked with the proud purchase of a JNF tree in the person's honour. It wasn't until adulthood that I began to understand that those feel-good faraway conifers, certificates for which papered the walls of my Montreal elementary school, were not benign — not just something to plant and later hug. In fact these trees are among the most glaring symbols of Israel's system of official discrimination — the one that must be dismantled if peaceful co-existence is to become possible.

The JNF is an extreme and recent example of what some call 'green colonialism'. But the phenomenon is hardly new, nor is it unique to Israel. There is a long and painful history in the Americas of beautiful pieces of wilderness being turned into conservation parks — and then that designation being used to prevent Indigenous people from accessing their ancestral territories to hunt and fish, or simply to live. It has happened again and again. A contemporary version of this phenomenon is the carbon offset. Indigenous people from Brazil to Uganda are finding that some of the most aggressive land grabbing is being done by conservation organizations. A forest is suddenly rebranded a carbon offset and is put off-limits to its traditional inhabitants. As a result, the carbon offset market has created a whole new class of 'green' human rights abuses, with farmers and Indigenous people being physically attacked by park rangers or private security when they try to access these lands. Said's comment about tree-huggers should be seen in this context.

And there is more. In the last year of Said's life, Israel's so-called 'separation barrier' was going up, seizing huge swathes of the West Bank, cutting Palestinian workers off from their jobs, farmers from their fields, patients from hospitals — and brutally dividing families. There was no shortage of reasons to oppose the wall on human rights grounds. Yet at the time, some of the loudest dissenting voices among Israeli Jews were not focused on any of that. Yehudit Naot, Israel's then environment minister, was more worried about a report informing her that 'The separation fence . . . is harmful to the landscape, the flora and fauna, the ecological corridors and the drainage of the creeks.' 'I certainly don't want to stop or delay the building of the fence', she said, but 'I am disturbed by the environmental damage involved.' As the Palestinian activist Omar Barghouti later observed, Naot's 'ministry and the National Parks Protection Authority mounted diligent rescue efforts to save an affected reserve of irises by moving it to an alternative reserve. They've also created tiny passages [through the wall] for animals.'

Perhaps this puts the cynicism about the green movement in context. People do tend to get cynical when their lives are treated as less important than flowers and reptiles. And yet there is so much of Said's intellectual legacy that both illuminates and clarifies the underlying causes of the global ecological crisis, so much that points to ways we might respond that are far more inclusive than current campaign models: ways that don't ask suffering people to shelve their concerns about war, poverty and systemic racism and first 'save the world' — but instead demonstrate how all these crises are interconnected, and how the solutions could be too. In short, Said may have had no time for tree-huggers, but tree-huggers must urgently make time for Said — and for a great many other anti-imperialist, postcolonial thinkers — because without that knowledge, there is no way to understand how we ended up in this dangerous place, or to grasp the transformations required to get us out. So what follows are some thoughts — by no means complete — about what we can learn from reading Said in a warming world.

Edward Said was and remains among our most achingly eloquent theorists of exile and homesickness — but Said's homesickness, he always made clear, was for a home that had been so radically altered that it no longer really existed. His position was complex: he fiercely defended the right to return, but never claimed that home was fixed. What mattered was the principle of respect for all human rights equally and the need for restorative justice to inform our actions and policies. This perspective is deeply relevant in our time of eroding coastlines, of nations disappearing beneath rising seas, of the coral reefs that sustain entire cultures being bleached white, of a balmy Arctic. This is because the state of longing for a radically altered homeland — a home that may not even exist any longer — is something that is being rapidly, and tragically, globalized. In March 2016, two major peer-reviewed studies warned that sea-level rise could happen significantly faster than previously believed. One of the authors of the first study was James Hansen — perhaps the most respected climate scientist in the world. He warned that, on our current emissions trajectory, we face the 'loss of all coastal cities, most of the world's large cities and all their history' — and not in thousands of years from now but as soon as this century. If we don't demand radical change we are headed for a whole world of people searching for a home that no longer exists.

Said helps us imagine what that might look like as well. He helped to popularize the Arabic word *sumud* ('to stay put, to hold on'): that steadfast refusal to leave one's land despite the most desperate eviction attempts and even when surrounded by continuous danger. It's a word most associated with places like Hebron and Gaza, but it could be applied equally today to residents of coastal Louisiana who have raised their homes up on stilts so that they don't have to evacuate, or to Pacific Islanders whose slogan is 'We are not drowning. We are fighting.' In countries like the Marshall Islands and Fiji and Tuvalu, they know that so much sea-level rise is inevitable that their countries likely have no future. But they refuse just to concern themselves with the logistics of relocation, and wouldn't even if there were safer countries willing to open their borders — a very big if, since climate refugees aren't currently recognized under international law. Instead they are actively resisting: blockading Australian coal ships with traditional outrigger canoes, disrupting international climate negotiations with their inconvenient presence, demanding far more aggressive climate action. If there is anything worth celebrating in the Paris Agreement signed in April 2016 — and sadly, there isn't enough — it has come about because of this kind of principled action: climate *sumud*.

But this only scratches the surface of what we can learn from reading Said in a warming world. He was, of course, a giant in the study of 'othering' — what is described in *Orientalism* as 'disregarding, essentialising, denuding the humanity of another culture, people or geographical region'. And once the other has been firmly established, the ground is softened for any transgression: violent expulsion, land theft, occupation, invasion. Because the whole point of othering is that the other doesn't have the same rights, the same humanity, as those making the distinction. What does this have to do with climate change? Perhaps everything.

We have dangerously warmed our world already, and our governments still refuse to take the actions necessary to halt the trend. There was a time when many had the right to claim ignorance. But for the past three decades, since the Intergovernmental Panel on Climate Change was created and climate negotiations began, this refusal to lower emissions has been accompanied with full awareness of the dangers. And this kind of recklessness would have been functionally impossible without institutional racism, even if only latent. It would have been impossible without Orientalism, without all the potent tools on offer that allow the powerful to discount the lives of the less powerful. These tools — of ranking the relative value of humans — are what allow the writing off of entire nations and ancient cultures. And they are what allowed for the digging up of all that carbon to begin with.

Fossil fuels aren't the sole driver of climate change — there is industrial agriculture, and deforestation — but they are the biggest. And the thing about fossil fuels is that they are so inherently dirty and toxic that they require sacrificial people and places: people whose lungs and bodies can be sacrificed to work in the coal mines, people whose lands and water can be sacrificed to open-pit mining and oil spills. As recently as the 1970s, scientists advising the US government openly referred to certain parts of the country being designated

'national sacrifice areas'. Think of the mountains of
Appalachia, blasted off for coal mining — because so-
called 'mountain top removal' coal mining is cheaper
than digging holes underground. There must be theories
of othering to justify sacrificing an entire geography
— theories about the people who lived there being so
poor and backward that their lives and culture don't
deserve protection. After all, if you are a 'hillbilly',
who cares about your hills? Turning all that coal into
electricity required another layer of othering too: this
time for the urban neighbourhoods next door to the
power plants and refineries. In North America, these
are overwhelmingly communities of colour, black and
Latino, forced to carry the toxic burden of our collective
addiction to fossil fuels, with markedly higher rates of
respiratory illnesses and cancers. It was in fights against
this kind of 'environmental racism' that the climate
justice movement was born.

Fossil fuel sacrifice zones dot the globe. Take the
Niger Delta, poisoned with an Exxon Valdez-worth of
spilled oil every year, a process Ken Saro-Wiwa, before
he was murdered by his government, called 'ecological
genocide'. The executions of community leaders, he said,
were 'all for Shell'. In my country, Canada, the decision
to dig up the Alberta tar sands — a particularly heavy
form of oil — has required the shredding of treaties with
First Nations, treaties signed with the British Crown that
guaranteed Indigenous peoples the right to continue to
hunt, fish and live traditionally on their ancestral lands.
It required it because these rights are meaningless when

the land is desecrated, when the rivers are polluted and the moose and fish are riddled with tumours. And it gets worse: Fort McMurray — the town at the centre of the tar sands boom, where many of the workers live and where much of the money is spent — is currently in an infernal blaze. It's that hot and that dry. And this has something to do with what is being mined there.

Even without such dramatic events, this kind of resource extraction is a form of violence, because it does so much damage to the land and water that it brings about the end of a way of life, a death of cultures that are inseparable from the land. Severing Indigenous people's connection to their culture used to be state policy in Canada — imposed through the forcible removal of Indigenous children from their families to boarding schools where their language and cultural practices were banned, and where physical and sexual abuse were rampant. A recent truth and reconciliation report called it 'cultural genocide'. The trauma associated with these layers of forced separation — from land, from culture, from family — is directly linked to the epidemic of despair ravaging so many First Nations communities today. On a single Saturday night in April 2016, in the community of Attawapiskat — population 2000 — 11 people tried to take their own lives. Meanwhile, DeBeers runs a diamond mine on the community's traditional territory; like all extractive projects, it had promised hope and opportunity. 'Why don't the people just leave?', the politicians and pundits ask. But many do. And that departure is linked, in part, to the thousands of

Indigenous women in Canada who have been murdered or gone missing, often in big cities. Press reports rarely make the connection between violence against women and violence against the land — often to extract fossil fuels — but it exists. Every new government comes to power promising a new era of respect for Indigenous rights. They don't deliver, because Indigenous rights, as defined by the United Nations Declaration on the Rights of Indigenous People, include the right to refuse extractive projects — even when those projects fuel national economic growth. And that's a problem because growth is our religion, our way of life. So even Canada's hunky and charming new prime minister is bound and determined to build new tar sands pipelines, against the express wishes of Indigenous communities who don't want to risk their water, or participate in the further destabilising of the climate.

Fossil fuels require sacrifice zones: they always have. And you can't have a system built on sacrificial places and sacrificial people unless intellectual theories that justify their sacrifice exist and persist: from Manifest Destiny to Terra Nullius to Orientalism, from backward hillbillies to backward Indians. We often hear climate change blamed on 'human nature', on the inherent greed and short-sightedness of our species. Or we are told we have altered the earth so much and on such a planetary scale that we are now living in the Anthropocene — the age of humans. These ways of explaining our current circumstances have a very specific, if unspoken meaning: that humans are a single type, that human nature can be

Naomi Klein

essentialized to the traits that created this crisis. In this way, the systems that certain humans created, and other humans powerfully resisted, are completely let off the hook. Capitalism, colonialism, patriarchy — those sorts of systems. Diagnoses like this erase the very existence of human systems that organized life differently: systems that insist that humans must think seven generations in the future; must be not only good citizens but also good ancestors; must take no more than they need and give back to the land in order to protect and augment the cycles of regeneration. These systems existed and still exist, but they are erased every time we say that the climate crisis is a crisis of 'human nature' and that we are living in the 'age of man'. And they come under very real attack when megaprojects are built, like the Gualcarque hydroelectric dams in Honduras, a project which, among other things, took the life of the land defender Berta Cáceres, who was assassinated in March 2016.

Some people insist that it doesn't have to be this bad. We can clean up resource extraction, we don't need to do it the way it's been done in Honduras and the Niger Delta and the Alberta tar sands. Except that we are running out of cheap and easy ways to get at fossil fuels, which is why we have seen the rise of fracking and tar sands extraction in the first place. This, in turn, is starting to challenge the original Faustian pact of the industrial age: that the heaviest risks would be outsourced, offloaded, onto the other — the periphery abroad and inside our own nations. It's something that is

40

becoming less and less possible. Fracking is threatening some of the most picturesque parts of Britain as the sacrifice zone expands, swallowing up all kinds of places that imagined themselves safe. So this isn't just about gasping at how ugly the tar sands are. It's about acknowledging that there is no clean, safe, non-toxic way to run an economy powered by fossil fuels. There never was.

There is an avalanche of evidence that there is no peaceful way either. The trouble is structural. Fossil fuels, unlike renewable forms of energy such as wind and solar, are not widely distributed but highly concentrated in very specific locations, and those locations have a bad habit of being in other people's countries. Particularly that most potent and precious of fossil fuels: oil. This is why the project of Orientalism, of othering Arab and Muslim people, has been the silent partner of our oil dependence from the start — and inextricable, therefore, from the blowback that is climate change. If nations and peoples are regarded as other — exotic, primitive, bloodthirsty, as Said documented in the 1970s — it is far easier to wage wars and stage coups when they get the crazy idea that they should control their own oil in their own interests. In 1953 it was the British-US collaboration to overthrow the democratically elected government of Muhammad Mossadegh after he nationalized the Anglo-Iranian Oil Company (now BP). In 2003, exactly fifty years later, it was another UK-US co-production — the illegal invasion and occupation of Iraq. The reverberations from each intervention continue to jolt our world, as do the reverberations from the successful burning of all that oil. The Middle East is now squeezed in the pincer of violence caused by fossil fuels, on the one hand, and the impact of burning those fossil fuels on the other.

In his latest book, *The Conflict Shoreline*, the Israeli architect Eyal Weizman has a groundbreaking take on how these forces are intersecting. The main way we've understood the border of the desert in the Middle East and North Africa, he explains, is the so-called 'aridity line', areas where there is on average 200 millimetres of rainfall a year, which has been considered the minimum for growing cereal crops on a large scale without irrigation. These meteorological boundaries aren't fixed: they have fluctuated for various reasons, whether it was Israel's attempts to 'green the desert' pushing them in one direction or cyclical drought expanding the desert in the other. And now, with climate change, intensifying drought can have all kinds of impacts along this line. Weizman points out that the Syrian border city of Daraa falls directly on the aridity line. Daraa is where Syria's deepest drought on record brought huge numbers of displaced farmers in the years leading up to the outbreak of Syria's civil war, and it's where the Syrian uprising broke out in 2011. Drought wasn't the only factor in bringing tensions to a head. But the fact that 1.5 million people were internally displaced in Syria as a result of the drought clearly played a role. The connection between water and heat stress and conflict is a recurring, intensifying pattern all along the aridity line: all along

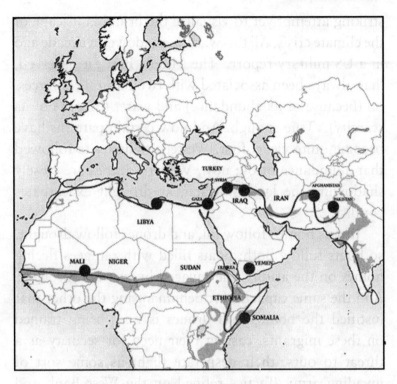

it you see places marked by drought, water scarcity, scorching temperatures and military conflict — from Libya to Palestine, to some of the bloodiest battlefields in Afghanistan and Pakistan.

But Weizman also discovered what he calls an 'astounding coincidence'. When you map the targets of Western drone strikes onto the region, you see that 'many of these attacks — from South Waziristan through northern Yemen, Somalia, Mali, Iraq, Gaza and Libya — are directly on or close to the 200 mm aridity line.' The dots on the map above represent some of the areas where strikes have been concentrated. To me this is the most

striking attempt yet to visualize the brutal landscape of
the climate crisis. All this was foreshadowed a decade ago
in a US military report. 'The Middle East', it observed,
'has always been associated with two natural resources,
oil (because of its abundance) and water (because of its
scarcity).' True enough. And now certain patterns have
become quite clear: first, Western fighter jets followed
that abundance of oil; now, Western drones are closely
shadowing the lack of water, as drought exacerbates
conflict.

Just as bombs follow oil, and drones follow drought,
so boats follow both: boats filled with refugees fleeing
homes on the aridity line ravaged by war and drought.
And the same capacity for dehumanising the other that
justified the bombs and drones is now being trained
on these migrants, casting their need for security as a
threat to ours, their desperate flight as some sort of
invading army. Tactics refined on the West Bank and
in other occupation zones are now making their way to
North America and Europe. In selling his wall on the
border with Mexico, Donald Trump likes to say: 'Ask
Israel, the wall works.' Camps are bulldozed in Calais,
thousands of people drown in the Mediterranean, and
the Australian government detains survivors of wars
and despotic regimes in camps on the remote islands
of Nauru and Manus. Conditions are so desperate on
Nauru that last month an Iranian migrant died after
setting himself on fire to try to draw the world's attention.
Another migrant — a 21-year-old woman from Somalia
— set herself on fire a few days later. Malcolm Turnbull,

the prime minister, warns that Australians 'cannot be misty-eyed about this' and 'have to be very clear and determined in our national purpose'. It's worth bearing Nauru in mind the next time a columnist in a Murdoch paper declares, as Katie Hopkins did last year, that it's time for Britain 'to get Australian. Bring on the gunships, force migrants back to their shores and burn the boats.' In another bit of symbolism Nauru is one of the Pacific Islands very vulnerable to sea-level rise. Its residents, after seeing their homes turned into prisons for others, will very possibly have to migrate themselves. Tomorrow's climate refugees have been recruited into service as today's prison guards.

We need to understand that what is happening on Nauru, and what is happening to it, are expressions of the same logic. A culture that places so little value on black and brown lives that it is willing to let human beings disappear beneath the waves, or set themselves on fire in detention centres, will also be willing to let the countries where black and brown people live disappear beneath the waves, or desiccate in the arid heat. When that happens, theories of human hierarchy — that we must take care of our own first — will be marshalled to rationalize these monstrous decisions. We are making this rationalization already, if only implicitly. Although climate change will ultimately be an existential threat to all of humanity, in the short term we know that it does discriminate, hitting the poor first and worst, whether they are abandoned on the rooftops of New Orleans during Hurricane Katrina or whether they are among the

36 million who according to the UN are facing hunger due to drought in Southern and East Africa.

This is an emergency, a present emergency, not a future one, but we aren't acting like it. The Paris Agreement commits to keeping warming below 2°c. It's a target that is beyond reckless. When it was unveiled in Copenhagen in 2009, the African delegates called it 'a death sentence'. The slogan of several low-lying island nations is '1.5 to stay alive'. At the last minute, a clause was added to the Paris Agreement that says countries will pursue 'efforts to limit the temperature increase to 1.5°c'. Not only is this non-binding but it is a lie: we are making no such efforts. The governments that made this promise are now pushing for more fracking and more tar sands development — which are utterly incompatible with 2°c, let alone 1.5°c. This is happening because the wealthiest people in the wealthiest countries in the world think they are going to be OK, that someone else is going to eat the biggest risks, that even when climate change turns up on their doorstep, they will be taken care of.

When they're wrong things get even uglier. We had a vivid glimpse into that future when the floodwaters rose in England in December 2015 and January 2016, inundating 16,000 homes. These communities weren't only dealing with the wettest December on record. They were also coping with the fact that the government has waged a relentless attack on the public agencies, and the local councils, that are on the front lines of flood defence. So understandably, there were many who wanted to change the subject away from that failure. Why, they asked, is Britain spending so much money on refugees and foreign aid when it should be taking care of its own? 'Never mind foreign aid,' we read in the *Daily Mail*. 'What about national aid?' 'Why,' a *Telegraph* editorial demanded, 'should British taxpayers continue to pay for flood defences abroad when the money is needed here?' I don't know — maybe because Britain invented the coal-burning steam engine and has been burning fossil fuels on an industrial scale longer than any nation on Earth? But I digress. The point is that this could have been a moment to understand that we are all affected by climate change, and must take action together and in solidarity with one another. It wasn't, because climate change isn't just about things getting hotter and wetter: under our current economic and political model, it's about things getting meaner and uglier.

The most important lesson to take from all this is that there is no way to confront the climate crisis as a technocratic problem, in isolation. It must be seen in the context of austerity and privatization, of colonialism and militarism, and of the various systems of othering needed to sustain them all. The connections and intersections between them are glaring, and yet so often resistance to them is highly compartmentalized. The anti-austerity people rarely talk about climate change, the climate change people rarely talk about war or occupation. We rarely make the connection between the guns that take black lives on the streets of US cities and in police custody and the much larger forces that annihilate so many black lives on arid land and in precarious boats around the world.

Overcoming these disconnections — strengthening the threads tying together our various issues and movements — is, I would argue, the most pressing task of anyone concerned with social and economic justice. It is the only way to build a counterpower sufficiently robust to win against the forces protecting the highly profitable but increasingly untenable status quo. Climate change acts as an accelerant to many of our social ills — inequality, wars, racism — but it can also be an accelerant for the opposite, for the forces working for economic and social justice and against militarism. Indeed the climate crisis — by presenting our species with an existential threat and putting us on a firm and unyielding science-based deadline — might just be the catalyst we need to knit together a great many powerful movements, bound together by a belief in the inherent worth and value of all people and united by a rejection of the sacrifice zone mentality, whether it applies to peoples or places. We face so many overlapping and intersecting crises that we can't afford to fix them one at a time. We need integrated solutions, solutions that radically bring down emissions, while creating huge numbers of good, unionized jobs and delivering meaningful justice to those who have been most abused and excluded under the current extractive economy.

Said died the year Iraq was invaded, living to see its libraries and museums looted, its oil ministry faithfully guarded. Amid these outrages, he found hope in the global anti-war movement, as well as in new forms of grassroots communication opened up by technology; he noted 'the existence of alternative communities across the globe, informed by alternative news sources, and keenly aware of the environmental, human rights and libertarian impulses that bind us together in this tiny planet.' His vision even had a place for tree-huggers. I was reminded of those words recently while I was reading up on England's floods. Amid all the scapegoating and finger-pointing, I came across a post by a man called Liam Cox. He was upset by the way some in the media were using the disaster to rev up anti-foreigner sentiment, and he said so:

> I live in Hebden Bridge, Yorkshire, one of the worst affected areas hit by the floods. It's shit, everything has gotten really wet. However . . . I'm alive. I'm safe. My family are safe. We don't live in fear. I'm free. There aren't bullets flying about. There aren't bombs going off. I'm not being forced to flee my home and I'm not being shunned by the richest country in the world or criticized by its residents.
>
> All you morons vomiting your xenophobia . . . about how money should only be spent 'on our own' need to look at yourselves closely in the mirror. I request you ask yourselves a very important question . . . Am I a decent and honourable human being? Because home isn't just the UK, home is everywhere on this planet.

I think that makes for a very fine last word.

JOHN BELLAMY FOSTER

Third Nature

Edward Said on Ecology and

Imperialism

Naomi Klein's wonderful essay on the numerous ecological implications that appear almost unconsciously in Edward Said's texts, forming part of their structural background — a perfect example of what he himself famously called a 'contrapuntal reading' — demonstrates that ecological themes were always just below the surface in his work, conditioning his own sense of resistance.[1]

---

[1] Said borrowed the notion of 'contrapuntal reading' from music. He used it especially in relation to Jane Austen's *Mansfield Park*, where a colonial-slave sugar plantation is the basis of the family's wealth and structures the plot without actually entering directly into the narrative. As Said explained, 'In practical terms, 'contrapuntal reading' as I have called it means reading a text with an understanding of what is involved when an author shows, for instance, that a colonial sugar plantation is seen as important to the process of maintaining a particular style of life in England. . . . The point is that contrapuntal reading must take account of both processes, that of imperialism and that of resistance to it, which can be done by extending our reading of the texts.' One can say that this phenomenon of the veiled reality of imperialism shows up in decolonising as well as colonising literatures. Said's own work brings out the violence

This is hardly surprising given his Palestinian heritage and his identification with the struggles there and throughout the Global South. Klein goes on to use this reading of Said on ecological imperialism to comment on the entire phenomenon of a world engulfed in Earth-system crisis, moving beyond the drought-ridden Palestine to Pacific Islands being submerged by sea level rise due to climate change — from which she takes her sardonic title 'Let Them Drown'.

It takes nothing away from Klein's remarkable argument in this respect, indeed it only serves to reinforce it, if we go on and recognize that in his last decade, particularly in his *Culture and Imperialism*, Said was drawn directly into the ecological discussion. This should not surprise us. He was altogether too sensitive a cultural critic of imperialism to fail to discern the degree to which ecology formed the background for many of the colonial and decolonial allusions to be found in writers from Austen to Yeats. In examining the literature of anti-imperial resistance in particular, and putting this into historical context, Said became acutely conscious of ecological themes. More importantly, he broke through the usual discussions and offered his own unique insights in this area. Relying on Alfred Crosby's *Ecological Imperialism*, Said explained that,

---

and physical dislocation of peoples due to imperialism. Klein shows that a contrapuntal reading of Said's work itself also reveals the deep ecological recesses of resistance in his thought. See Edward Said, *Culture and Imperialism* (New York: Vintage, 1993), p. 66.

Wherever they went Europeans immediately began to change the local habitat; their conscious aim was to transform territories into images of what they had left behind. The process was never-ending, as a huge number of plants, animals and crops as well as building methods gradually turned the colony into a new place, complete with new diseases, environmental imbalances, and traumatic dislocations for the overpowered natives. A changed ecology also introduced a changed political system.[2]

This ecological remaking of colonial territories in the image of the colonizer's own territory was tied to the unequal development that the imperial powers imposed on most of the world. Referring to the work of Marxian geographer Neil Smith, Said saw imperialism as culminating in a process that 'universally commodifies all space under the aegis of the metropolitan centre'.[3] This was then justified within the geopolitical ideology of imperialism in the work of thinkers like Halford Mackinder, who saw it all as a result of national conditions of fertility, differentiated ecological zone, climates, and races.[4]

Most important in Said's discussion was his treatment of what Hegel, Marx, and Lukács called 'second nature', resulting from the transformation introduced by human

[2] Said, *Culture and Imperialism*, p. 225.

[3] Said, *Culture and Imperialism*, p. 225; Neil Smith, *Uneven Development* (Athens: University of Georgia Press, 2008).

[4] On Mackinder see John Bellamy Foster, 'The New Geopolitics of Empire', *Monthly Review* 57, no. 8 (January 2006), pp. 1-18.

production, counterposed to 'first nature'. From a position of resistance to imperialism, Said explained, such a second nature was clearly an *imperialist second nature*. There could be no return to first nature. What was required therefore was the creation of a *third nature* that would both restore (in part) what had existed before and would transform the human relation to nature into something new:

To the anti-imperialist imagination, our space at home in the peripheries has been usurped and put to use by outsiders for their purpose. It is therefore necessary to seek out, to map, to invent, or to discover a *third* nature, not pristine and pre-historical ('Romantic Ireland's dead and gone', says Yeats) but deriving from the deprivations of the present. The impulse is cartographic [a kind of remapping of the land], and among its most striking examples are Yeats's early poems collected in 'The Rose', Neruda's various poems charting the Chilean landscape, Césaire on the Antilles, Faiz on Pakistan, and Darwish on Palestine —

Restore to me the color of face
And the warmth of body,
The light of heart and eye,
The salt of bread and earth . . . the Motherland.[5]

---

[5] Said, *Culture and Imperialism*, 225-226; Mahmoud Darwish, *Splinters of Bone* (Greenfield Center, New York: Greenfield Review Press, 1974), 23.

The restoration of the land and the ecology was a constant theme of revolutionary anti-colonialism. 'One of the first tasks of the culture of resistance', Said observed, 'was to reclaim, rename, and reinhabit the land. And with that came a whole set of further assertions, recoveries, and identifications, all of them quite literally grounded on this poetically projected base.' In this way he pointed to a poetic aesthetic of ecological resistance in the periphery. The fact that it was predicated on the need for a *third nature* made the 'emergence of an opposition' in the periphery at the same time the articulation of a new revolutionary ecology, an alternate relation to the earth. It meant transforming 'the imperialized place' of the present into a renewed and more developed social commons.[6]

Said's powerful explanation of how 'space at home' had been usurped seemed to recast the images from Marx's treatment of primary ('so-called primitive') accumulation, and what Marx had called 'usurpation of the common lands' accompanying the 'expropriation of the agricultural population from the land'. Said also seems to have recast Marx's treatment of the alienation of nature, in referring to how imperialism had 'alienated the land' and thus 'alienated people from their authentic traditions'.[7]

All of this gave a more radical meaning to ecological aspirations, in which the recovery of the human

---

[6] Said, *Culture and Imperialism*, 67, 226, 239.
[7] Karl Marx, *Capital* (London: Penguin, 1976), pp. 877-885, *Early Writings* (London: Penguin, 1974), pp. 318-19; Said, *Culture and Imperialism*, pp. 33 and p. 225.

connection to the earth, and therefore to labour, and to human community — as well as to past traditions — played an indispensable role in the urge to resist and create a new cultural reality. The sense of expropriation, of theft, of robbery, of alienation of the earth, and estrangement from past, Said recognized, existed among people struggling everywhere; but this alienation was especially prevalent amongst those seeking to cast off the imperialist yoke. Lukács, in his discussion of 'lost transcendence' in his *The Theory of the Novel* — Said pointed out — had argued that 'every novelistic hero . . . attempts to restore the lost world of his or her imagination'. This was a reflection of the deep alienation of nineteenth century society, in which the rifts could not be healed.[8]

Culture and Imperialism, despite its scholarly form, was meant as a work for contemporary struggle. Although much of it focused on eighteenth and nineteenth English literature, it leaped forward into a more global, more resistance-based perspective of the twentieth century. Here Said identified the ecological perils now emerging on a planetary level, and the importance of ecology in mustering the needed global revolt from below. He referred to 'the immense range of global forces (including what has been called "the death of nature")' producing the contemporary period of crisis and change. In this context, he contended,

[8] Said, *Culture and Imperialism*, pp. 156-67; Georg Lukács, *The Theory of the Novel* (Cambridge: MIT Press, 1971), pp. 35 ff.

The two general areas of agreement nearly everywhere are that personal freedoms should be safeguarded, and that the earth's environment should be defended against further decline. Democracy and ecology, each providing a local context and plenty of concrete combat zones, are set against a cosmic backdrop. Whether in the struggle of nationalities or in the problems of deforestation and global warming, the interactions between individual identity (embodied in minor activities like smoking, or using of aerosol cans) and the general framework are tremendously direct, and the time-honoured conventions of art, history and philosophy do not seem well suited for them . . . . More reliable now are the reports from the front line where struggles are being fought . . . . The major task, then, is to match the new economic and socio-political dislocations and configurations of our time with the startling realities of human interdependence on a world scale.[9]

There can be no doubt that what Said was calling for here was the creation of a *third nature* on a global scale, a new cultural-material-reality, reflecting a sustainable relation between human beings and the earth, and a world of substantive equality. This is of course was closely related to the society of associated producers as conceived by Marx.[10]

Said knew that the human and cultural resources

[9] Said, *Culture and Imperialism*, p. 330.
[10] On Marx's ecological conception of socialism see John Bellamy Foster, 'Marxism and Ecology', *Monthly Review* 67, no. 7 (December 2015), p. 4.

for this change were to emerge first in the periphery, in a process of *de-imperialism* — if humanity were to have a meaningful future at all. He had a sense of being a permanent exile, but he drew from this the personal resources for an alternative vision of human liberation. 'Just as human beings make their own history', he wrote in the closing paragraph of *Culture and Imperialism*, 'they also make their cultures and ethnic identities. . . . Survival in fact is about the connections between things.'[11] It was necessary finally to heal the rifts — social, ecological, and cultural — in our disconnected world.

---

[11] Said, *Culture and Imperialism*, p. 336; compare Karl Marx, *The Eighteenth Brumaire of Louis Bonaparte* (New York: International Publishers, 1991), p. 15.

GHASSAN HAGE

On the Relation between Racial and Environmental 'Othering'

When someone on Facebook drew my attention to Naomi Klein's Edward Said lecture, I read it with a mixture of excitement and regret. Excitement as it dealt with the relation between racism and the ecological crisis, a topic I have been researching and thinking about for some time: it was simply delightful to have a piece which covered so many important key issues in so little space, while also offering many original thoughts on the subject and pointing to fruitful areas of research. I experienced regret for basically the same reason. I had just handed in a manuscript of a book dealing with the topic to Polity Press.[1] I would have loved to have read

---

[1] Ghassan Hage, *Is Racism an Environmental Threat?*, Polity Press, 2017.

Klein's piece before I finished writing my book so I could think my work with it. I am therefore very pleased that Vijay Prashad invited me to comment on this piece as it gives me the opportunity to take a couple of Klein's ideas and walk with them and against them towards what I think are shared horizons.

One of the lecture's key arguments highlights the relevance of Said's study of 'othering' for an understanding of the ecological crisis. This is because as Naomi Klein put it:

> . . . once the other has been firmly established, the ground is softened for any transgression: violent expulsion, land theft, occupation, invasion . . . What does this have to do with climate change? Perhaps everything.

I fully agree with this 'perhaps everything', as it points to something that I think is exceptionally important, namely the intrinsic connections between the invasion, occupation, domination and exploitation of an 'othered people' and the invasion, occupation, domination and exploitation of an 'othered nature.'

To be sure, an ecological crisis is by definition something all-encompassing. It relates to everything located within it from the very moment it becomes categorized as an ecological crisis. This is why we also refer to it as 'environmental'. When a crisis is deemed 'environmental' it is no longer a crisis in a specific relationship that one can have with a particular x or y. It becomes a crisis of the very environment, or milieu, in which we can have relationships to x or y. Take for example a garbage-collection crisis that has been taking place in Lebanon since 2015. It began as a breakdown in the garbage disposal system due to its complex entanglement with the logic of economic and political sectarian competition in the country. As people began to dispose of their rubbish anywhere they could, the garbage started fouling the already polluted environment. Soon the street smells, the ugly appearance of sea and mountain vistas, the contaminated rivers, permeated everything, causing inconveniences, discomfort and disease. 'Garbage disposal' was no longer an unmanageable relation to garbage; it became constitutive of the entire social atmosphere. It affected the way people worked, their mood, where children played, what could be eaten and where one could eat, how and where one could exercise, and more.

It is a similar all-encompassing quality that defines the 'environmental crisis' we are facing globally today. Because of this, it is *always* possible to demonstrate that any social phenomenon is related to the environmental crisis. From such a perspective, however, we cannot tell if there is a difference between the relation between ecological crisis and racism and the relationship between the environmental crisis and the fluctuations of the stock exchange. In both set of relations we can imagine processes independent from each other coming to intersect, precisely because of the all-encompassing nature of the environmental crisis. The relation between the two is here imagined as external and conjunctural.

However, by raising the question of commonality in forms of othering Klein raises the prospect of a different, internal and far more intimate relation. Here racism and the ecological are never independent of each other. Their commonality and their interaction is not conjunctural but part of their very nature.

Othering, as Said, and Klein, point out, is a process of categorization grounded in particular practices of domination and exploitation. The first thing that follows from this is that 'othering' is not, except rarely, a scholastic exercise. It is always imbued with the relations of power and instrumentality in which the process is inserted. So, we need to be attentive not just to the fact that there is othering but to exactly what kind of othering is being done and how it is done. In *Is Racism an Environmental Threat?* I look at the racist usage of animal metaphors as one of the many interfaces where the imaginaries of the natural/ecological and the human/racial meet. I register a historical shift in the dominant mode of othering Arab Muslims: from 'cockroaches' to 'wolves'. This is, of course, not an absolute change. Many racists still refer to Muslims as 'cockroaches'. But there is no doubt that there is an increased reference to them as 'wolves'. It can be noted that both cockroaches and wolves have been themselves subjected to extermination, and as categories of othering are used metaphorically as part of a language of extermination. Yet, one does not gaze at a cockroach the same way one gazes at a wolf. The top down gaze that is part of the exterminatory gaze directed at cockroaches is absent in the 'wolfish mode of othering' which involves a more 'horizontal' gaze. Attention to such details, I argue, gives us access to what Nietzsche calls the 'sense of power' that is inscribed in the process of othering. There are many other ways in which the process of othering can be sociologically and culturally differentiated. The above was to simply give an example of the important domain that Klein opens by making that link. It is especially important if we come to understand both the ecological crisis and the racial crisis as coming to terms with an 'other' that is increasingly experienced not only as 'unruly' and 'ungovernable', but also as 'overwhelming'. That is why, I give particular attention to what I call 'fantasies of reversal': fantasies where humans imagine themselves being overwhelmed and dominated by nature, and where white Europeans imagine themselves being colonized by those they have been colonising.

The second thing that follows once we establish a commonality between racial and ecological forms of othering is that we need to locate a generative principle of categorizations and practices that is shared between them. Here, to me, lies the central importance of Klein's reflections. They invite us to ask: what is the generative principle behind both the racist and the ecologically destructive practices? She points to a clear direction in looking for an answer. She feels that speaking of 'the age of humans', 'the anthropocene' as an overarching principle is of the same order as speaking of a generalized greedy or short-sighted human nature. It disallows us to speak of human created social systems, such as 'capitalism, colonialism and patriarchy', which is where we should be looking for our common generative principle. Otherwise, she argues, we are bound to let these systems 'off the hook'. What's more it also disallow us from thinking the existence of actually existing alternative human systems that 'insist that humans must think seven generations in the future; must be not only good citizens but also good ancestors; must take no more than they need and give back to the land in order to protect and augment the cycles of regeneration.' These systems existed and still exist, but they are erased every time we say that the climate crisis is a crisis of 'human nature' and that we are living in the 'age of man'.

There are many resonances between the above and what I propose in my book. There is a particularly strong common ground in her analysis of fossil fuel's 'sacrifice zones'. The idea that,

> The thing about fossil fuels is that they are so inherently dirty and toxic that they require sacrificial people and places: people whose lungs and bodies can be sacrificed to work in the coal mines, people whose lands and water can be sacrificed to open-pit mining and oil spills.

For Klein, these sacrificial places and sacrificial zones cannot come to exist without 'intellectual theories that justify their sacrifice (. . .): from Manifest Destiny to Terra Nullius to Orientalism, from backward hillbillies to backward Indians.'

Like Klein, using Marx's concept of primitive

accumulation, I highlight the fact that capitalism has always been dependent on a sphere of 'primitive', 'savage' and 'uncivilized' forms of accumulating wealth. In a sense, I argue, the history of capitalism is a history of oscillation between a legalized accumulation and the civilized cosmopolitan spaces in which it flourishes and a primitive accumulation with its savage social, cultural and ecological spaces where otherness is exploited, and often over-exploited to the point of extermination. The more capitalism is suffering from a crisis of profitability the more it tends towards over-exploitation and the uncivilized culture and politics that comes with it. Indeed we can say, the election of Donald Trump in the United States is a good case of capital needing to sever its links with its classical cultured political elite, the so-called 'establishment', and re-articulating itself with a vulgar, ecologically destructive, sexist and racist political leadership that can more easily enact savage forms of accumulation.

Nonetheless, what I consider as the final generative mechanism of both this racism and environmentally destructive ethos is what I call 'generalized domestication'. This is not a universal human nature but it is nonetheless a universal mode of being or mode of existence: a mode of being inserted in the world such that the primary relation we have to the world is an instrumental, managerial one. As an anthropologist I agree with Klein that there are other, actually existing, modes of existence in the world that are not instrumentalist in the way generalized domestication is. But what characterizes the pre-modern societies studied by anthropology is not so much that they are not capitalist, nor that they are not instrumentalist about nature, but rather that they encompass a plurality of modes of existence which tamper and minimizes the impact of their instrumentalism: such as relations of reciprocity and relations of mutuality. Thus, if capitalist modernity is at fault here it is because it has formed such a strong relation of affinity with this generalized domestication making it prevail in a form of symbolic violence that makes us see it as if it is the only mode of existence and disallow us to think of alternative modes of existence. It is to such plurality of modes of existence that we need to strive.

RAFIA ZAKARIA

Empire and the Overpass

The sea has been on the move in Karachi. Over the decades, as the city has burst its seams, it has moved farther and farther away into the distance. If you arrive very early in the morning at the beaches closest to the city and drive out until the road ends, you can sometimes see how this banishment of the sea is accomplished. Solitary lines of trucks, weighed down by their cargo of gravel and sand, empty their loads, making marsh into land. The land they make is sold at high prices, entire neighbourhoods of the wealthy stand on it, proud high houses encircled by high walls, looking defiantly at the sea they have pushed so far out into the distance. They are not afraid.

The poor are not afraid either, or perhaps fear is a luxury they cannot afford. As Karachi has grown from a few million to ten million and now to twenty million, droves of them descend on city beaches on the last day of every week, even more on Eid or on Independence Day. Two or three or four fall off the thin, worn seats of motorcycles, ten or eleven spill from small Suzuki trucks. Everyone is dressed in their best, the women in bright floral prints or black burkas yell at children who do not listen. Surrounded by husbands and fathers and uncles, guardians of their broods, they make their way out to the water. Groups of just men come too, some holding hands, their beards and their long trousers wet with salt spray. All of them jump in, let the waves splash their feet and their faces. The city is behind them, they know, and so too must be the filth that is born of it.

They are wrong. The houses and high-rises closest to the ocean are not connected to the city sewage system. The waste that accrues from them flows, untreated and unhindered, into the ocean. The elite clubs that have opened up to cater to the ocean-side-dwelling wealthy, dump all their waste into the ocean also, all the grease from wedding banquets that feed a thousand, all the pesticide-laden groundwater they use to water their acres of lawns in the desert of Karachi.

The Lyari and Malir Rivers, both of which empty into the same sea, bring their own gifts. Their banks further up into the city are lined with factories, leather tanneries, paper mills, medical and chemical manufacturing operations of all kinds, legal and illegal. Everything that they do not use, everything that is created in the process of making something else, is pushed into the ocean. This is the toxic brew in which the poor beach goers of Karachi, the young children, the expectant mothers, the old aunts and the scowling, solemn fathers, bathe when they immerse themselves into the ocean. They also leave their own gifts behind. At the end of every weekend, their Styrofoam cups, their bottles of soda, the plastic bags in which they brought their snacks, their lost shoes and all their discarded detritus covers the beach, joining the tons of toxicity at the edge of the city.

* * *

The poor of Karachi who so eagerly and ardently plunge themselves into an ocean that is fetid with the effluents and excrement of the city are what Naomi Klein would call the 'sacrificial people' of our planet. They include economic migrants, arriving from small villages dotted all over the country for jobs in the metropolis. Many of them are single men who have never seen the ocean, who spend their days inside airless factories, labouring at jobs that pay nearly nothing. When something is left of this nothing, they come to the sea.

Then there are those who have fled to the city to escape the war in Pakistan's north, their villages pillaged first by the Taliban, then by American drones and ultimately by the 'clean-up' operations carried out by the Pakistani military. They too come to Karachi, live on its outskirts, their families crammed together in the homes of relatives. Like millions of others, they search for jobs and if they find them, and perhaps even if they do not, they come to the sea.

The luckiest of both of these groups hope that they will progress on to other seas. Many among the economic and war weary migrants who come to Karachi hope to migrate. The lucky ones who do, graduate into the economy of fossil fuel extraction, to desolate oil rigs in the Persian Gulf. Their sacrificial bodies will toil and take from the earth the oil that lies at heart of the world's conflicts. It is in the extraction of oil that they locate the fulfillment of their small dreams, the house to be built, the sons to be educated. The stories of these men are stories of survival, and in the midst of its urgent demands, it is easy, as Edward Said did, to discard the concerns of environmentalism as a 'bourgeois conceit'. What is easy, however, is not always true.

***

Mai Kolachi was a fisherwoman who lived by the Indus Delta. Today her name adorns an overpass that connects the city's busy port to the highways that snake through the remainder of Pakistan. It is a peculiar irony that the name of a woman who harkens back to the origins of Karachi as a sleepy fishing village is attached to a project that has involved the destruction of crucial portions of its ecosystem, but that is how it is. Unsurprisingly, the seeming urgency of constructing an overpass that required the dislocation of slum dwellers and the evisceration of mangrove forests was necessitated by war. In 2001, when NATO troops poured in next door to fight the war in Afghanistan, the port of Karachi became the node at which all the supplies for them were brought to shore. The transport of these crucial materials of war that would kill thousands across the border required an overpass that would permit the NATO supply tankers to bypass city traffic and gain fast access to the highway. In this way, multi-million dollar Mai Kolachi Overpass Project was born.

So it was that the ingredients required to kill in Afghanistan necessitated first the destruction of environmental ecosystem in Pakistan. The overpass was routed through the lush mangrove forest at Chinna Creek, destroying what was a natural rainwater drainage ditch. Locating the Overpass in the rain drain thus reduced the capacity of rainwater to flow directly into the ocean. This means that the oldest portions of the city, now also some of the poorest, are flooded by rainwater every single monsoon. The fetid water that has nowhere to go stands in the streets and in homes for days, becoming infested with mosquitos and flies. These in turn breed diseases, leaving hundreds sickened by cholera, malaria and dengue fever.

The mangrove forest that once was also disappeared from along the sides of the road that connects to the overpass. So too has its capacity to serve as a barrier for approaching hurricanes and cyclones. The migratory birds, cranes and pelicans that stopped in the forest every year coming south from Central Asia have no place to stop. Where there was once something living and beautiful, there is now a road whose primary goal is to transport the building blocks of warfare.

Perusing through old newspapers from the time of the construction of the Mai Kolachi Overpass, I found a quote by one of its most vociferous opponents, Parween Rehman, an urban planner and environmental activist who headed up the Orangi Pilot Project (located in one of Karachi's largest slums). 'All land reclamation needs to be stopped immediately', Rehman had held unequivocally. 'The backwaters should be returned to their natural state and a flyover constructed where Mai Kolachi passes over the natural drains. At least one flyover should be made for the fish and mangroves. Why just for the cars? Fish also need to cross to the other side. We've killed them and finished them off.'

None of that ever happened, of course, but more tragedy did. Just like the fish and trees that had been a casualty of the $700 million dollar Mai Kolachi overpass, Parween Rehman was herself killed, a little over a decade after she had given that interview and as she had continued her opposition to projects that destroyed environmental ecosystems, scapegoated the poorest of Karachi's citizens and exposed land grabs by the city's powerful. Parween Rehman was gunned down by assailants on 13 March 2013. Over three years later, the case was still dragging on, with no one yet punished for the killing.

The Mai Kolachi Overpass must have transported hundred of thousands of tons of military equipment in the decade and a half since the NATO invasion of Afghanistan. It is now a fixture of Karachi's urban transportation system, a whole generation grown without knowledge of a time when it did not exist. In 2011, the outline of a sharp new building emerged against the skyline of the overpass. The new US Consulate of Karachi, the newspapers boasted, was built

according to the 'latest technology'. At its inauguration,
then US Consul General William Martin said that the
new building 'clearly reflects the enduring relationship
between America and Pakistan and is a commitment
by the American people and the government to stand
with Pakistan in the long term.' Speaking specifically
to the location of the new building, Consul Martin
added, 'This is a historic and important move. I am
looking forward to showing the people of Sindh and
Balochistan our new consulate complex. Our relocation
enables us to continue building a strong and mutually
beneficial relationship between the American people
and Pakistanis.'

* * *

There is much that is written and much that is said
about the War on Terror, Pakistan's role in it. It is rare,
however, that the story of terror is linked to the violence
done to ecosystems, to slum-dwellers and to the poor
and desperate and those who advocate for them. Naomi
Klein refers to just this when she writes, 'there is no way
to confront the climate crisis as a technocratic problem,
in isolation. It must be seen in the context of austerity and
privatization, colonialism and militarism.' The story of
the Mai Kolachi Overpass reveals the interconnections
between Karachi's endless drive for land reclamation,
the exogenous forces that demand destructive shortcuts,
and the ravaged ecosystems that are left behind in their
wake.

Stories like that of the Mai Kolachi Overpass are scattered through the injured terrain of our warming world. If the south of Pakistan, its ports and coastal belts had to be made available for transport supply lines, its north was patrolled by drones. Many of the areas that were patrolled by these remote controlled bombers have also had the basis of their livelihoods drastically altered by resource extraction. Communities in North Waziristan, a part of the fetishized and bombed out 'tribal lands', once depended on subsistence agriculture. Then mining came along, with gypsum mines and men began to work there, abandoning agriculture and developing a new exploitative relationship with the land that birthed them. When mining operations shut down or required less labour, there were no jobs. Men left, for Karachi or for the Gulf. Fatherless sons were left to the machinations of the Tehreek-e-Taliban Pakistan, who offered a possibility of crude and cruel revenge against larger forces and a raped and pillaged landscape.

The task of the climate activist of the future is the task of telling these stories, of, as Klein puts it, 'overcoming these disconnections, strengthening the threads, tying together our various issues and movements.' It is only in telling these stories, replete as they are with both the tragedy of loss typified by the construction of an overpass in Karachi, that there can be hope for a truly inclusive and truly radical movement against climate change. It is only when this corrective is taken seriously, when the case for interconnection and urgency can be made via the story of a road named after an old lady but which killed much that was old, much that was treasured and much that was living, that a kinder, future can be hoped for.

MASTURAH ALATAS

Hair Conditioning

My hair is long and wavy. It is changeable, like the weather and the sea; sometimes smooth and silky, sometimes frizzy and knotty. There are products to remedy the latter condition — organic ones like coconut oil, and other chemical concoctions of commercial conditioners.

I once stood next to a young woman, observing her as she was surveying bottles of conditioner on a shelf in a supermarket in Kuala Lumpur. She finally chose one.

'Ah, she cares about her hair, like I do', I said to myself. 'But what was her hair like?'

I couldn't tell because she was hijabed. Polyester. A nice plum colour. I wondered if there was research on the health condition of hair that was covered with thick, synthetic fabric for long hours, day in and day out, year after year for the rest of its life, in hot, tropical climates. Did her head perspire under the cover? How often did she wash and condition her hair? What would happen if women who habitually wore hijab started balding? What would the men say?

Maybe the woman buying conditioner didn't even perspire that much because she spent most of her time in air-conditioned environments, in the office or at home.

Perhaps even her ride to work in her own car or in a taxi or by monorail was in the cool, artificial, dry comfort of air-conditioning.

I know, though, that heat does not counsel reason. I've seen men from New York's Wall Street to Singapore's Raffles Place corseted up in jackets and ties on the most scorching days, and hijabed women under wide straw hats working in the fields in Malaysia. The difference is that those financial district men probably wander around in the hot outdoors only for a short while before they bustle back inside to their air-conditioned cubicles tucked away in skyscrapers. The peasant women, on the other hand, are under the sun for many hours.

Habit is the perpetuation of convention. Once you accept something, you persist with it. You make yourself get used to it. You live with it. You live *in* it. Italian gives us a word with the many shades of meaning for living. From the Italian verb *abitare* (to live in, to inhabit) comes *abito* (habit, as in what a nun/cleric wears), *abitazione* (house) and *abitudine* (habit, as in what we habitually do). But the fact that wearing the hijab, like the business suit, has become routine for many does not stop those for whom it is not a habit from feeling hot when they look at a covered woman standing in the hot sun.

The Muslims of Indonesia, along with those of Malaysia and Singapore, are what makes that corner of Southeast Asia the region with the most number of Muslims in the world. Today more Muslim women in Indonesia and Malaysia wear the hijab than those who do not. You don't need to check the statistics to know

76

this. It is enough to walk around the cities and the villages, the suburbs, the offices and the shopping malls to see this.

That hijabed women in Malaysia have become the subject of contemplation for me in recent years means that I have noticed a change. It was not like this before. Even in Singapore, which has a majority ethnic Chinese, non-Muslim population, the Malay women are covering up. The moment I am made to feel the odd one out, I am being othered as much as I am othering. I am being made aware that many have chosen to conform, and I am becoming aware of a difference that is distancing.

When did the change happen? Rather than ask why, which would lead me into inconclusive exegetical arguments about *tafsir* (interpretation), I prefer to ask when. Again, I can check the statistics, but memory tells me that when I was in school in Singapore in the seventies till the mid-eighties, none of my teachers wore the hijab. None of my friends did either and neither did their mothers.

If you look at archive pictures of the mid-eighteenth century up to the 1970s, you will come across the unhijabed wives of Malay Sultans as well as students, civil servants and peasants who are not wearing the hijab.

What is also striking about these archive pictures is that you have images of Malay women in traditional clothing wearing a headscarf. But their shoulders are sometimes bare, and hair shows through the scarf, which may slip. So the headdress was not fixed.

Today, instead, covering has come to mean completely obliterating from sight and hiding under layers of cloth tightly secured with pins, every single trace of hair so that the whole wrap becomes completely wind proof and not a single strand peeps out. As far as the torso is concerned, every single inch of skin from the chin down to the hands is covered.

How did the Malay women of previous epochs keep cool? Paintings and photographs show that women in the villages tied batik sarongs around their chests, the cotton cloth falling just below their knees. They kept their shoulders bare and their heads without caps as they jumped into cool — and hopefully not crocodile-infested — rivers and seas. Since these villages were ruled by Malay sultans before and after the arrival of the Portuguese, the Dutch and the British, we can deduce that there was little or no influence coming from European colonizers on the way Malay women dressed for swimming.

If the contemporary hijabing of Malay women is yet another indication that traditions change and cultural symbols are never fixed, then we have to conclude that many a Muslim woman in Malaysia today believe that their uncovered ancestors over the centuries must have made a mistake in the way they lived their Islam, as did the Malay rulers. Considering that Islam arrived in Southeast Asia through missionary activity and trade starting from the 12th century, we have so many centuries of Muslims making a mistake about how the *Quran* and hadiths are to be interpreted regarding the way women should dress. And only in the late 20th century did they begin to rectify it.

The fact remains that over the past three decades, the heads of Malay women have become more colourful with polyester. Today, as in past centuries, just as the not wearing of the veil cuts across social class, so does the wearing of it. I am seeing more and more female tourists from Saudi Arabia and other Muslim countries along with the local women swimming in Malaysian seas and the pools of five star Malaysian hotels clad in full niqab or chador. The more fashionable ones wear the burkini looking like superheroes choosing to save and please no one but themselves, or so a portion of the feminist rhetoric claims.

We could collocate these changes in the attire of Malaysian Muslim women with political events in the world — the 1979 Iranian revolution; the Dakwah or Islamization movement in Malaysia during the 1970s and 1980s of which Anwar Ibrahim, then a youth leader who later became Culture Minister and Agriculture Minister, was a great proponent; the first 1987 Palestinian intifada; September 11; and the subsequent strengthening of ties between Saudi Arabia, the US and their allies against al-Qaida and Iran.

But here is the paradox. If Muslim women are covering up because they feel they are doing the right thing — they are righteous in that sense — and if Malay women are part of the labour force, are educated, have economic independence and thus play a central role in society and in society, why, as Malaysians become more covered and more Islamic by their own definition of what Islamic is, is their country becoming more corrupt? In 2015, the 1Malaysia Development Berhad (1MDB) Scandal came to light in which Prime Minister Najib Tun Razak was found with around $700 million in his personal bank accounts, a sum thought to have been siphoned from the 1MDB fund. Why has righteousness gone in one direction, towards Malay women, but not in other important ones, such as the leadership of the country?

I've always asked myself whether the working Muslim women in the urban centres of Malaysia and Singapore would wear hijab if air-conditioning was not easily available almost everywhere. The removal of air-conditioning might have at least two effects: 1) Muslim women would start taking off the hijab and 2) there would be fewer carbon emissions.

What those hijabed women I saw working in the fields under the hot sun are telling us is that it is possible to work without air-conditioning. But they work and live in the countryside, which is still greener than the cities. Land is stripped of its trees to build cities, and it is the cities which have the most concentration of air-conditioning. The British used to build villas and bungalows on the coolest spots in the verdant, breezy Malaysian hills; sturdy, concrete structures with large windows shaded by awnings and surrounded by verandas. Of all the things of the colonial past to imitate, the way the British built homes to keep cool has not been one of them. Many of these houses have not even been conserved. It is too late now for Malaysia to rely on the shade of its trees to keep cool. Keeping cool in the world always entails a human cost and a cost to the environment. And this keeping cool is, paradoxically, making the world warmer.

Instead, if hijabed women decide to take off their veils because they are fed up of feeling hot, this would tell us that they are not just uncovering their heads but they are opening their minds. It would be a symbolic gesture, a return to a time in Malaysia when Malay women had not adopted the headscarf as a fixed garment in public. It would be a sort of collective, symbolic gesture to demonstrate that they are not so susceptible to conventional or hegemonic Islamic practices, and to a notion of how the country should develop which is contributing to the climate crisis.

But would the transformation from veil on to veil off be painless the way chillies suddenly and quietly change colour from green to red? Who benefits most from keeping the heads of Malay women covered? Who has the most to lose? If keeping Malaysia's women hijabed is of prime importance, then they have a powerful weapon on their heads and they can start calling ultimatums. There's another haze, we take our veils off. A flood? Off. Corruption? Off.

Clothing has always been used to make political statements, from yellow Bersih (Malay for clean) t-shirts against corruption to the Femen protesting topless. But how much of a scandal do these gestures really cause? One is truly scandalized when one is afraid of losing one's identity. We become easily scandalized when our notion of who we are is questioned. And fear makes us conform.

The simple gesture of removing the veil or not always wearing it makes a very powerful statement — 'we are changing the climate, the climate can change us'. There has been a lot of talk about the veil — the choice to wear it, the banning of it. But there has been very little talk in terms of the choice of women to remove the hijab as a strategy which shows, as Naomi Klein writes, the 'connections and intersections' with various 'systems as othering'.

Since Malaysia's independence from the British in 1957, the nation's government has been in the hands a Malay majority coalition. Deforestation was carried out in an aggressive way especially after Mahathir Mohamad came to power in 1981. When once challenged over the matter of deforestation, he said, 'Are they asking us to give up development, so that the rest of the world can breathe?'[1] Mahathir has since changed his tune, and calls for also 'legal logging' to be limited and controlled in the interest of 'preserving our forest'.[2] But the fact remains that a large percentage of Malaysian land, including the state of Sarawak, has been subject to rapid deforestation, and has therefore contributed to regional pollution and haze caused by forest fires, an increase in

[1] Alex Kirby, 'Malaysia's Solar Power Costs Dear', BBC, 17 November 2003.
[2] Dr. Mahathir Mohamad, 'Deforestation', 27 November 2014 (http://chedet.cc/?p=1533).

flooding and soil erosion, the displacement of resident indigenous populations and endangering the orangutan for whom the forest is its natural habitat.

The situation in Indonesia is worse. When somebody lights a match in an Indonesian rainforest, Singapore and Malaysia can't breathe for weeks.

In Italy, when I travel by train from the Marche region to Rome, it is quite likely that the window will frame a succession of varying pictures. If it is summer, fields of sunflower, grano duro wheat, olive groves, vineyards. Sunflower oil, pasta, olive oil, wine — all things that are very important for the Italian economy.

In Malaysia, the picture is different; or rather, it stays the same. It is possible to see the same scenery from a train window even after crossing one state border into another. Hectares and hectares, plantations the size of entire regions, of interminable oil palm. Malaysia is one of the largest producers of oil palm. But oil palm plantations sprouting up on deforested land like hair transplants are destroying peat land and causing floods.

When Giacomo Leopardi wrote in his poem, *L'infinito* (1819), that the countryside hill of his birthplace, Recanati, was always dear to him, he was in a position to say 'always' because the hill had not changed much in his lifetime. It turns out that the hill he was looking at is almost the same one we look at today. Our view is not blocked by skyscrapers or a new crop. At most, our vision is hindered by a mere hedge. And it is this hampered view that stimulates the mind to look beyond.

But how many sustainably developed Leopardian hills are there left in the world? While the future of the planet as we know it may not seem infinite, maybe the future of thinking and ideas is — such as the idea of how a hill should develop or the idea of preserving the traditional way Malay women of past centuries covered their heads.

To drown in the immensity of thinking is the only kind of drowning that is, to use Leopardi's word, sweet.

SHALINI SINGH

Others in Arms

I write this while nursing a hacking cough. India's capital is choking. The combination of various irritants — burning of coal, leaves, wood, firecrackers — exacerbated by a mysterious revolt by the winds that help disperse the deadly cocktail, built up to an uncomfortable static atmosphere for the inhabitants. No one is immune. The winds do not discriminate between Lutyen's Delhi and Laxmi Nagar, Anand Niketan and Anand Vihar. There is no 'safe zone' to escape to and no covert magic air Disneyland to be found. The rich queue up at mask shops at India's most expensive retail locations, buying their need for clean air. These masks are decorated with top designer patterns, costing over Rs. 2000. Having bought their masks, they get into their air-conditioned cars. The poor, meanwhile, wrap inexpensive cotton bandannas or handy handkerchiefs around their mouths, as they walk the streets.

In the midst of over 25 million people gasping for air, came an announcement. The Prime Minister — Narendra Modi — announced that currency in 500 and 1000 rupee notes would immediately cease to be legal tender. The date — 8 November 2016 — is symbolic.

The number 8 is seen within numerology as a karmic equalizer. It is made up of two mirror-image circles that represent creation and destruction or the sign of infinity when viewed horizontally. A collective incredulous shudder greeted the announcement, and then came a shot of pain along Indian society's spine. The next morning onward would see the nation's people along its socio-economic ladder, mostly on the lower rungs, queue up outside banks to deal with this new reality, positioned as eliminating black money from the country, all for a 'white' future.

Discomfort came in many different forms. Working people had to stand in line and forgo their daily wages. They stood patiently in serpentine queues to exchange or withdraw cash. They worked for days on credit, because their employers did not have change for the new shiny pink Rs. 2000 note. Prudent women had to reveal wads of cash hidden from alcoholic or abusive husbands in different parts of their homes. These precious rainy day funds, secreted away for a better tomorrow, now became a part of the demonetization fiasco. Some even died — nearly a hundred deaths directly linked to demonetization were reported across the country. Elderly waiting in line collapsed, while housewives committed suicide and bank employees succumbed to stress. They were 'collateral damage' to this policy.

For people like us, plastic cards saved the day, while my car's fuel tank remained unusually full. Petrol pumps, it turned out, as well as government hospitals were allowed to accept old notes till a later date. There were a few odd stories about people helping their domestic staff open bank accounts, while some got their workers to store extra cash till further arrangements could be made.

As I write this exactly a month later, peering above the laptop screen at the television set, news breaks about all manner of corruption amidst the chaos. The most significant being the cases of bank employees getting caught in money conversion frauds. The average Indian brain is quite the Houdini — always manages to find a way around and out of everything — our *jugaad* wrongly encrusts our true talent. But that's another story.

In the elite circuits, I have overheard guffawing whispers from the rotund-bellied about agent commissions and 'home delivery' of converted money for those who could afford it. At a film screening, a nattily-dressed social media celebrity told her tittering friends how the move had left her and the domestic help at the 'same level' — 'can you believe it', she said, 'that we both had just 300 rupees in our purses? I told her today there is no difference between you and me.' Sure, that sounds like quite the level playing field.

In advanced yoga, *sarvangasana* or the shoulder stand pose aids in delivering blood from the lower half of the body to the upper half, thereby leading to healthier, equitable circulation of the vital fluid that balances the entire being. But anyone who practices yoga, (perhaps now more so given that 21 June has been assigned as International Yoga Day), would know that done wrongly, the pose can end up injuring the neck or spine or both.

Demonetization has revealed fault lines that will, in all probability, change forever how the people of this country view the vital element that runs their lives. The rich would know how poor the poor are and the poor would know how rich the rich are. What then? Time will tell how this ambivalence plays out when, hopefully, the chaos settles.

***

This takes me back to Goa of 2010. Goa is India's smallest state, with its 101-km long coastline, known far and wide for its tourism. I was reporting under an environment fellowship about the drawbacks of the tourism policy and market pressures on its land development. It was interesting to explore the Sunshine State with a degree of incision that eventually revealed to me several issues.

Goa's famous *susegad* spirit was being threatened by the very people who were attracted to that spirit in the first place.[1] Who are the authors of the threats? The moneyed classes, especially from Delhi and Mumbai, wanted their own real estate along the coastline. These flats and holiday homes caused a strain on the limited

---

[1] *Susegad* is a word derived from the Portuguese word *sossegado*, meaning quiet.

natural resources in Goa, and, in turn, led to violent clashes between local residents and tourists.

In its capital city, Panjim, I peered closely at the mounting protests against mining activities that adversely affected people. As the voices grew louder, my digging into the issue got deeper. Over shared meals and intense conversations, I began to feel less of an outsider and more like one of the locals. I extended the stipulated stay of my assignment. It was hard to leave. Rama, a middle-aged local tribal activist, agreed to let me travel with him and experience things first hand. It took us more than a day to journey to his home in Colamb village, a thickly forested area of south Goa. His large family welcomed me with generous quantities of watery *dal* and starchy rice, quietly forgoing parts of their share, laughed at my horror at discovering the house being in the open and surrounded by wild animals, not to mention all electricity promptly going off at sunset every day.

My sheltered urban upbringing summoned doubts within me about my safety from the animals. We all slept in rows on a large floor with a frayed bed-sheet for cover and an open starry sky for ceiling. Whether it was the wind rustling at the door or a cheetah, I didn't want to guess. If the fear of even the tiniest creepy-crawlies kept me awake in a well-lit room back home in the city, then this experience had awakened even deeper fears. I closed my eyes. The next morning dawned like a personal triumph. Rama took me to a small hidden spring pond near his home and gestured we could drink directly from it. 'Really? You don't need to filter this?', I asked cupping my hands as he grinned, shaking his head. It was a moment of bonding despite our acknowledged different worlds. The water tasted divine, an antithesis to what followed. As we journeyed in his old open jalopy through mining areas, swathes of green trees covered in a dull red dust looked like dried up blood, and open mud pits resembled purposeful wounds. We spoke to families whose children suffered from respiratory trouble like pneumoconiosis because of suspended dust particles in the air – common to mining areas. In another tribal family's home in the village, a wall carrying a deep gash caused by a mining blast in the area, threatened to cave in. A foreboding air marked out the barricaded check-posts of the mining areas, men against their own, while one gutsy truck driver allowed us to hide in his truck as he drove inside the excavation sites. The stories repeated with different characters and locations in the mining area of the northern part of the state. The issue wouldn't have, perhaps, garnered as much traction as it did later because the argument would be that mining happens all over the world and people living in those areas get affected. That there are sustainable ways to mine the earth is never on the table. Even when it does appear, it is more often as smoke screen to cover over the nastiness of the industry.

What came to the surface was the stark inequality of the industry. This could not be ignored. Goa has a small population and a high literacy level. The top mining companies were raking in more profit than the revenue of the entire state. Goa was exporting more iron-ore to

China than it was producing, thereby implying gross illegalities. Corruption was at the heart of the accounts. My interviews with the then chief minister of the state and mining companies were far from friendly. I wrote the story as it revealed itself.

One afternoon in Panjim, I chatted with Rama and an academic-activist named Seby over a delicious fish *thali* meal. We talked about daily life, about health and about the constant resource wars that structured their lives. This fight has been going on for decades. In 1993, Rama and his father went to the courts to defend their land, which had been leased to the mining companies by the state. The miners had been selling the fertile soil from their village to another village. This was pillage of an old sort. The action by Rama and his father got an illegal mine closed. The government arrested father and son and put them in jail. Their case went on for three years. They eventually reached a compromise. Rama's father said that the village soil had to be retained. 'We wage our battles with a smile', said Rama. My mouthful of impatient queries was met with that calm sentiment.

* * *

Such patience and perseverance echoed what I had observed in Mendha Lekha, a tribal village in Gadchiroli, Maharashtra, a year later. This village is surrounded by the war between the Naxals and the State — one of India's biggest internal conflicts. Despite this, Mendha Lekha was able to peacefully secure its rights under the historic Forest Rights Act (FRA) of 2006. It was one of the first villages to do so. The FRA has not — a decade later — lived up to its potential. Nonetheless, it provided essential rights where few existed previously. To win these rights, the residents of Mendha Lekha were led by Mohan Hirabai Hiralal — a Gandhian activist — who helped them empower themselves to manage and generate income from forest produce, especially bamboo, which was a contentious point between the people and government. I was struck by the form of governance in the village. The villagers followed a 'governance by consensus' model, where a decision is taken only when every person is convinced. This model includes collective counselling of any alcohol addict in the village. I had not seen anything like this before.

While the villagers of Mendha Lekha won some rights from the FRA, the villagers of the eastern state of Odisha suffered the weight of the South Korean giant POSCO project. POSCO was dangled by the central government as the country's largest such investment. The weight of the State sat heavily on the villagers. They would find something in common with the people of Hebron, Gaza, Standing Rock (North Dakota) and coastal Louisiana. The Palestinian concept of *sumud* — steadfastness — defines the courage of the people in all these places as they have fought the violence of the State and of corporations. The State did not want the Rs. 52,000 crore steel project to be delayed. In 2011, two villages in the district of Odisha where POSCO would be located claimed that their rights were not settled under the Other Traditional Forest Dwellers part of the FRA. They said that they had not given their consent for the project. The steel factory would, in setting up a port on the Bay of Bengal, destroy the fishing possibilities that have given small fisher communities a sustainable livelihood for as long as they remember. It would also destroy the betel gardens that provide several families with modest earnings. Odisha prides itself on its betel leaf, which is used in traditional offerings and in popular consumption. Both fish and betel would lose to benefit steel.

POSCO and what it would mean for the area divided the people into opposing camps. Those who said that they wanted the project became 'outsiders' as far as those who opposed the project were concerned. The same land that gave the people a sense of identity was used to create 'transit' camps for the villagers who took a pro-POSCO position. They became the 'no-where' people who could not go back to their original village for fear of their own people. The environment ministry's enquiry committee acknowledged the fault line that opened up within the villages, 'POSCO has, unfortunately, divided the villagers of the eight project villages into opposing camps and has created a great deal of hostility within the villages, in what was earlier a peaceful, agricultural area.'

A year later, in 2012, I spent three months in South Korea on a press fellowship, covering the presidential elections. One of the field trips included a visit to the POSCO headquarters, one of the country's biggest 'development drivers'. Unofficially we learnt of the devastation to the local population and natural resources that the project caused when it was allowed to be set up there. On the other side, it also contributed to the country — the size of one large Indian state and relatively homogeneous in faith — in becoming economically powerful.

The argument is always that there will be some casualties in the larger scheme of things. The reactive point is, are you willing to be that casualty? Who is? Why them? Why are the sacrificial people and lives never from among the ones who perpetuate the idea that sacrifice is necessary for development?

India, a relatively poor and greatly unequal country, stands at the point of muscling forward to claim a place among the 'developed' nations at a time when progress and patriotism are buzzwords. Nowadays, at times, eerily so. The idea isn't to react or romanticize a side, but to reflect on the costs of progress. If we need to produce more, how does one do it without causing damage? Can there be a balance? Could it begin with listening to the voices on different sides? Could the very issues that divide us bring us together? Can Others turn Brothers? Could the idea of a platform like the World Social Forum find more space in our conscience and engagement?

***

Growing up in a nuclear family in Delhi, I learnt two things from observing a Marxist grandfather committed to the cause of science popularization, and a conservative mother committed to the cause of her family's well being. In his sense of the ideal, my grandfather treated domestic help of the house no differently, offering to bring a chair for the woman who looked after me as a child or inviting the spot boys of my aunt's film-making crew to sit with us at the dining table, much to the muted horror of my mother who felt such gestures caused confusion when the rest of the world treated them differently. Both meant no ill will. My mother mothers all the stray puppies in the colony or unabashedly hugs our help in moments of affection, while my stoic grandfather did not engage beyond giving them fair wages or extending basic courtesies. But both respected each other's views. There wasn't a clash over whose way was right or fair. We lived with the duality. I was free to pick up what resonated. Perseverance and pragmatism became my takeaways.

In the last four years, I have developed a focus on gender issues. I have written about the new national policy for Indian women to the every day life of a lone disabled woman activist. Nonetheless, till things change as we want them to I won't walk or drive alone if it is late at night or if the streets are empty. When I got attacked at Lodi Garden — in the cocooned heart of Delhi — earlier this year, I lodged a police complaint as part of my civic duty, went back to the area with the police team to assist them in the process, tweeted the FIR, tagging relevant officials, including the Chief Minister and the well-connected chattering crowd I passed by on my evening walks in the park. My feminism may not change everything in my life, but it surely allows me to keep hacking away at things that are distressing. I knew nothing would come off the complaint given the circumstances. But the next day, to my pleasant surprise, I saw a new street light in the dark area where I had been attacked. 'In a gentle way, you can shake the world', said Mahatma Gandhi.

On 16 December 2013, a young woman was gang raped in Delhi. It evoked a great outpouring of sentiment — from sadness to outrage. Angry young women and men marched up to the corridors of power. Was this merely a sense of entitlement amongst the consuming sections? Or was there more to it than that? Was there a link to the villagers whose lives were being destroyed with each corporate deal? Was this an Indian Spring? I did a story on the psychology of the young dissenters. To better understand them I went to see a famous political psychologist. He told me, 'Iran, Egypt, India, Turkey are becoming regimes of despair. There are huge pockets of despair and narcissism. In the reality of despair, you sense it but deny it by building different walls (narcissism) - page 3 news, luxurious holidays, virtual reality, hyped talks of development, lifestyle diseases of the rich.'

There was no real Indian Spring, but disaffection can grow in different, unknown ways. The tempo is hard to predict. The social fractures might move at any time.

Stuck in yet another anxiety-inducing traffic jam the

other day, I called up a close friend — who's equally aware and mocking of his birth as a Hindu Brahmin and identifies with American Conservatism, which he learned during his education in the United States. I vented my frustration and anger at him. 'One day', I said, 'the *aam aadmi* is going to be very, very angry and demand their rights. I sure hope to be there when that happens.' My friend sang Faiz Ahmed Faiz's 1979 poem, written against the suffocation of the Zia dictatorship in Pakistan. The tag line is *hum dekhenge* — we will see.

Lazim hai ke hum bhi dekhenge
Wo din ke jis ka waada hai
Jo lauh-e-azl mein likha hai

It is true that we too shall see
That day which has been promised
Which is written with God's ink

I don't think our friendship would have the same charge and challenge if we identified with the same side. Sure, there would be comfort in the agreements, but also, no challenge and growth without the disagreements. What underlines the equation is respect for the difference and an open ear to another perspective.

There is a rise of the vehement Right in different parts of the world today, paralleled with a decline of the Left that grapples with a lack of vision, and a 'viable model' as some say. In a democracy, the plurality of voices is an ideal. Countries such as India were founded on that principle. Could the Indian Left, then, do as it had done during the freedom struggle and during so much of India's post-colonial period — be the voice of conscience for a nation hurtling towards possible dangerous futures?

Surely, as we must oppose any kind of censorship on our freedom of expression, we could learn from Nassim Soleimanpour, a young playwright in Iran who could not leave his country till his play, *White Rabbit Red Rabbit* (2010), became a smash hit. The play travelled the world, to be performed in at least fifteen languages. Soleimanpour then moved to Berlin. The concept of his play effectively subverts all known equations of power, beginning at the intellectual level, where even how theatre was reviewed had to be introspected upon.

Could we, following scientist Stephen Hawking, demand an urgent response from the world's elite to the dangerous policy direction taken by the powers that be? Should we not, as writer George Monbiot asks, demand that we reclaim our humanity? Why should wanting to care or empathize be considered unfashionable or naive? Why should idealism be uncool?

When you stand at the divide between the haves and have-nots, men and women, rich and poor, this caste and that religion, one country and another, hoping that what you stood at instead was a bridge, one that enabled easier access between the two, chronicling to your best ability what you see as being part of the fourth pillar of democracy, I don't know if we have easy answers or can profess to a clear vision today. But for now, when we try to tell stories that we feel should matter too, could our own fraternity not swipe us away with the dismissive, oft-heard, 'Oh, you're one of those bleeding heart *jholawallah* (hippie communist) types'?

SUSAN ABULHAWA

Before the Last
River

On 2 December 2016, I set off with about thirty US military veterans on a bus from New York City to stand in solidarity with an epic historic Native American battle to stop the Dakota Access Pipeline, the *black snake*. Over 38 hours later, we arrived at Standing Rock, North Dakota, a 'fossil fuel sacrifice zone', as Naomi Klein would say.

The standoff began in April, when a small group of Lakota Sioux gathered in a prayer protest where the pipeline was set to burrow under the Missouri River, threatening the only remaining water source for the Sioux Nation of North Dakota. The Sacred Stone camp, led by LaDonna Bravebull Allard, was among the first, and their message was simple, 'we came to protect the water'. Within weeks, the water protectors grew into a coalition of over 300 Native American tribes, and they received solidarity from indigenous and oppressed nations around the world. Flags representing this convergence of marginalized peoples lined the entrance to the encampment, called Oceti Sakowin (Seven Council

Fire), which reached as many as 14,000 individuals. Energy Transfer Partners (ETS), the company behind the pipeline, tried to remove the water protectors, resorting to attack dogs and later to spraying people with water cannons in sub-zero weather. But the Sioux and their friends remained.

It was in these parts, not far from Oceti Sakowin, that white conquest began its final campaign to consolidate control of the whole of North America, when US General George Armstrong Custer discovered gold in 1874 in the sacred Lakota Black Hills, which had been encompassed in the Fort Laramie Treaty of 1868 as Lakota territory 'in perpetuity'. Although the terms of the treaty were clear and the Black Hills were central to Lakota spiritual life, the government of President Ulysses S. Grant launched a merciless military campaign to seize Lakota territory on behalf of mining companies and land speculators. It would be another war in the so-called 'Indian Wars' which had begun centuries prior. Atrocities followed, like the massacre at Wounded Knee Creek, accomplishing the errands of power. By the end of the Indian Wars, which continued until the turn of the century, an estimated sixteen million natives had been killed, hundreds of indigenous cultures and languages obliterated, and over 90% of the North American bison wiped out. Today, more than a century later, the drama of the assault on native peoples is still being played out in the same places, for the same reasons. ETS, the local police and their hired paramilitary are the heirs to Custer's legacy of unrelenting colonial malfeasance,

susan abulhawa

and the unarmed water protectors carry forth the spirits of their heroic leaders, like Crazy Horse, arguably the greatest warrior America has ever known.

NOTHING SO ELEGANT AS A RATTLESNAKE'S TAIL

At the camp, armoured vehicles of private military and state police power perched on the hilltop. Their spy drones buzzed overhead all day and their floodlights shone through the night. Oceti Sakowin was not perfect. It was not a utopia where love prevailed and everyone got along. And I learned that individual members of the tribes are not immune to corruption and greed. But being there, one could see the contours of a better society, a less destructive way to be in the world. There was a prevailing mood of community, purpose, and communal living. Hope, creativity, mystery and a sense of the spiritual were central. People worshiped through dance and song. They prayed, meditated and gave offerings of sage and tobacco to sacred fires that burned continuously. They kept warm as best they could, cooked and ate and cleaned. One woman gave birth. It was understood that everyone would be taken care of, everyone would eat, and everyone would work and contribute in accordance with ability.

Naomi Klein spoke of such societies, where life is traditionally organized in step with nature's cycles of regeneration. In contrast to western social philosophies — which are generally predicated on the primacy and exceptionalism of the human experience, and human

102

dominion over all there is — those that emerged from indigenous or First Nation peoples, and which are available to us principally in the form of proverbs and observable ways of life, are informed by a humility that places humans in a larger natural order. They form a cultural ethos that holds the natural world in sacred trust for future generations, and rest on philosophies such as this Native American proverb:

Treat the earth well. It was not given to you by your parents. It was loaned to you by your children.

The ecocultural mores of these societies emphasize not only environmental protection for future generations, but also personal responsibility to non-human life.

We must protect the forests for those who can't speak for themselves such as the birds, animals, fish and trees.
— Qwatsinas (Hereditary Chief Edward Moody), Nuxalk Nation

Their way of knowing recognizes the interconnected dependency of the living.

The tree inhales the air we exhale, and we inhale what the tree exhales. So we have a common destiny with the tree.
— Floyd Red Crow Westerman, Sioux elder

It looks upon life with awe.

susan abulhawa

There is nothing so elegant as a rattlesnake's tail.
— Navajo proverb

. . . and weaves elements of the environment even into the individual's sense of identity.

I was warmed by the sun, rocked by the winds and sheltered by the trees, as other Indian babes. I can go everywhere with a good feeling.
— Geronimo

If it were possible to graph cultural narratives, the West would have a line graph, endlessly reaching for greater heights on a y-axis, unaware or unconcerned for what is required to push up from the x-axis. In contrast, the First Nations' cultural narratives would be circular, the integrity of arcs stabilized by intersecting human, animal and plant life, much as a dream catcher might look.

You have noticed that everything an Indian does is in a circle, and that is because the Power of the World always works in circles, and everything tries to be round. . . . The Sky is round, and I have heard that the earth is round like a ball, and so are all the stars. The wind, in its greatest power, whirls. Birds make their nest in circles, for theirs is the same religion as ours.
— Black Elk, Oglala Sioux Holy Man

THE LAST TREE

The people at Oceti Sakowin were there for a green earth, with thriving wildlife, roaring rivers and blue skies. Those on the hilltop would add more veins and arteries to sustain a fossil fuel monster wilting our planet, coating and suffocating it in spilled and burned oil. There, the earth and all it contains of life is to be had, mined, pumped, logged, siphoned, eaten, worn, burned, hung on walls.

Sacrifice zones like Standing Rock — where life and capitalism are juxtaposed in the fullness of their contradictions; where birth and killing contest the same space; where empire stands with death machines in guard against the misery that sustains it — are everywhere now. The Amazon, our planet's breathing apparatus and home to its greatest treasure of biodiversity, is slowly and irreversibly disappearing.[1,2] Logging companies, ranchers who feed behemoth western appetites for meat, oil and chemical companies and retailers are driving the massive deforestation, resource depletion, pollution, land and water degradation, and speciocide.[3,4] One company alone, Texaco (later rolled into Chevron), dumped 18 billion gallons of toxic waste, spilled millions of gallons

[1] http://adsabs.harvard.edu/abs/2013AGUSMGC21A..05S
[2] http://www.sciencemag.org/news/2015/08/meat-eaters-may-speed-worldwide-species-extinction-study-warns
[3] https://www.theguardian.com/environment/2009/may/31/supermarkets-amazon-cattle-deforestation-greenpeace
[4] https://www.theguardian.com/environment/2009/may/31/cattle-trade-brazil-greenpeace-amazon-deforestation

of crude oil, and left hundreds of unlined open-air pits full of hazardous waste in pristine forests, rivers and streams in the Ecuadorian Amazon. The devastation to wildlife, fauna, and indigenous peoples is ineffable. Activists, journalists, and lawmakers who try to protest are swiftly silenced by Chevron's hired goons and militias.[5] They are in places like Bhopal, India, where a Union Carbide spill littered the streets with hundreds of thousands of dead or debilitated people, cows, birds, dogs and cats. In Bangladesh, where over 3,500 garment workers toiled 90 to 100 hours a week for $0.12 to $0.24 per hour in Rana Plaza, a garment factory for western clothing companies, 1,337 people were crushed to death or never found in the rubble when the factory collapsed on them. The little known backstory is one of massive dumping of toxins from these textile factories that have been polluting rivers, making people sick, killing off fish stocks and inundating rice paddies with toxic wastewater unremittingly for years.[6] Companies like Coca-Cola, Nestlé, Veolia, and PepsiCo are likewise looting water from around the world to sell in single use plastic bottles that end up in landfills and oceans where they kill off thousands of fish and sea birds. Monsanto, the largest producer of genetically modified organism (GMO), is slowly replacing our planet's natural food source with patented seeds that are eradicating natural seeds

[5] http://www.mintpressnews.com/chevron-blasted-for-rainfo rest-chernobyl-and-mob-like-tactics-to-silence-critics/177640/
[6] http://www.nytimes.com/2013/07/15/world/asia/bangladesh-pollution-told-in-colors-and-smells.html?_r=0

developed over millennia, dismantling long-established farming, and selling us dangerous food. Their ability to take over agriculture is buttressed by the strong fist of the US military or by supranational capitalist institutions like the World Bank, the International Monetary Fund, and the World Trade Organization. The magnitude of criminality is difficult to contemplate. Dow Chemical, Ford Motor Company, DynCorp, Halliburton, DuPont, G4S, Kellogg, Brown and Root, Lockheed Martin, Pfizer, Philip Morris, Cargill and many more are leaving some of the worst scars on our planet and they have devastated whole societies for profit. The future of our world, food, water, trees, wild life, marine life, oceans, and ecological sustenance are becoming *de facto* commodities of multinational corporations and an elite minority, who use the machinations of government to subvert societies.

Naomi Klein writes, 'This is happening because the wealthiest people in the wealthiest countries in the world think they are going to be OK'. These are men and women, well-fed and in fine clothes, who collude in a class-consciousness predicated on assumptions of their primacy and reach for all there is. It is not difficult to name those who, with chilling forethought and unfathomable disregard, driven by little but immediate self-interest, will sacrifice whole nations of orangutans, leopards, gorillas, elephants, and people; millions of crawling, buzzing, hopping, swimming and flying lives; great masses of ancient forest; timeless rivers and oceans, sky and air. Yet, there is no viable structure to hold them accountable. We do not even have words or language sufficient to describe such metastatic crimes, nor are there real penal commitments specific to those who commit them.

A Cree proverb says, 'Only when the last tree has died, the last river has been poisoned, and the last fish caught will we realize we cannot eat money.'

But we need not wait for the last tree. Our atmosphere, that powder of gas that deflects cosmic heat, radiation and other profound harm from our planet, has eroded and soon might become too thin to protect our world. For many, like the besieged in Gaza, the water is already too polluted or too expensive to drink. It is predicted that unless there are fundamental changes in agriculture, in less than six decades, the topsoil will be too depleted to grow food.[7] Already, an increasingly barren ocean is burying nations, like those of Solomon Islands.

WHAT, THEN, IS TO BE DONE?

Maybe there are lessons from Standing Rock. The decision of LaDonna Bravebull Allard and her friends to put their bodies in the way of massive machines backed by enormous wealth and power, was an inspiring commitment that tapped into humanity's growing anxiety over the degradation of the natural world. A few honest reporters further galvanized worldwide solidarity as reports and images of private security using attack dogs against unarmed protectors circulated the globe through

[7] http://world.time.com/2012/12/14/what-if-the-worlds-soil-runs-out/

social media. The camp grew as individuals arrived from around the country, many of them activists in other movements. Money poured in to sustain the protectors. More cameras and reporters brought the world's eyes there. Then came a few thousand US military veterans, like the ones with whom I shared a bus from New York.

Then, Oceti Sakowin won the battle.

Authorities had set a 5 December deadline for people to evacuate the camp. On 4 December, the Army Corps of Engineers denied the easement permit necessary for ETS to continue construction of the pipeline. They cited legal and scientific technicalities. Of course, capitalism is resilient and there remain ways that ETS can eventually move forward, but everyone agrees that the easement denial had nothing to do with legality or science. The easement was denied because people found their power. This was a struggle of the Sioux and everything that happened was under their leadership. But alone they were no match for the military and financial might of a corporate state. The victory at Standing Rock had to do with convergence of commitment, solidarity, activism, and technology. The arrival of veterans was also not insignificant. It signaled the possible transfer of military science and power from the ruling elite to the people, threatening a dangerous precedent. For activists, it also showed us that moral clarity does not rest with victims or specific groups, but that it is an available option to every individual, regardless of past choices.

There was euphoria when news came that the easement was denied. One US Army veteran reminded us that 'tomorrow is General Custer's birthday'. And he added, 'I wish he could see that his army has switched sides.' In speaking with those veterans over several days of being stranded together through a blizzard, I came to learn that all of them were broken in one way or another by the military. They emerged with various degrees of knowing that their lives were used as fodder for profit, and they showed up alongside Black Lives Matter and Palestinian activists, among others. Klein said that 'tying together our various issues and movements' would be at the heart of our success, and that's what we saw at Standing Rock, where converged issues of police brutality against black and brown bodies, the occupation of Palestine and Iraq, military PTSD, indigenous rights and water pollution.

But I believe it will take more than that. If we aspire to a more just and sustainable future, then one of the great tasks before us is to make clear to *the wealthiest people in the wealthiest countries in the world [who] think they are going to be OK,* that their privilege, their fortunes, and their physical safety are not predestined. Our task is to use all means available to us, at all levels of activism, hacktivism, sabotage, and violence if necessary, to ensure the obliteration of their impunity.

AMITAV GHOSH

Afterword

What Nutmeg Can Tell Us
About Globalization

For many years the word 'globalization' was used as shorthand for a promised utopia of free trade powered by the world's great centres of technological and financial innovation. But the celebratory note has worn thin. The word is now increasingly invoked to explain a widespread recoiling from a cosmopolitan earth. People in many countries are looking nostalgically backward, toward less connected, supposedly more secure times.

But did such an era ever exist? Was there ever an unglobalized world?

The question struck me during the final hours of the American election of 2016, when I happened to be traveling by ferry in the Maluku archipelago of Indonesia. Once known as the Moluccas, this corner of the world is considered remote even within Indonesia. Two time zones removed from Jakarta, it straddles one of the most seismically volatile zones on earth; many of its islands are active volcanoes rising steeply out of the sea. In size they range from small to minuscule. Surely

111

if ever there were a global periphery, it would be here.

Yet for millenniums these islands have been at the forefront of global history. This is because their volcanic soils have nurtured two miraculous trees, which grew nowhere else on earth: One is Syzygium aromaticum, which produces the clove, and the other is Myristica fragrans, of which nutmeg is the seed and mace the seed's lacy outer covering.

For thousands of years these spices were among the world's most sought-after commodities, making the sultans of the 'Spice Islands' famously wealthy. Cloves from around 1700 B.C. have been found at the site of a settlement in Tell Ashara, Syria. To get there, they would have had to travel more than 6,000 miles, through the ports of the Indian Ocean and overland through Mesopotamia. At every stop, their price would have multiplied hugely. In Renaissance Europe, the value of some spices was thousands of times more than at their point of origin.

The Republic of Venice possessed a virtual monopoly on the spice market in the Mediterranean for centuries. Although pepper and ginger, mainly from India, accounted for the bulk of the cargo, cloves, nutmeg and mace from the Moluccas commanded much higher prices by weight.

It was in hopes of bypassing Venice and the Middle East that the monarchs of Spain and Portugal funded the great voyages of the age of discovery. The Portuguese mariners who pioneered the sea route to the Indian Ocean brought with them not just their religion but also the prevalent European faith in monopolies. This notion was alien to the trading cultures of the Indian Ocean, where the rulers of the major ports had always vied with one another to attract as great a variety of merchants as possible. The Portuguese, and the Spanish, Dutch and English who followed them, were unheeding of these traditions: They never veered from their quest for monopolies, especially amid the vulnerable islands of the Moluccas.

A murderous, decades-long struggle ensued in which the competing European powers were pitted against one another, as well as the people of the Moluccas. In the process the English gained their first Asian possession, a pair of tiny islands, Ai and Run, part of a Moluccan chain called the Bandas.

In the end it was the Dutch who won, but at the cost of atrocities that included an attempted genocide. In 1621, on the orders of the Dutch East India Company's governor general, some 14,000 of the Banda Islands' estimated 15,000 inhabitants were slaughtered or taken into slavery. Two years later, officials of the Dutch East India Company beheaded 10 Englishmen and a number of others in a mass execution that is known as the Massacre of Amboyna.

Although the bloodshed sealed the Dutch hold on the East Indies, the British did not relinquish their claim to the island of Run until several decades later. So eager were the Dutch to get them out of the Moluccas that in 1667 they agreed to an exchange in which the English gave up their claim on Run in return for the recognition of their right to territories that included another island on the far side of the planet — Manhattan.

This connection may be forgotten in New York, but it is remembered by many in Run, which is today a sleepy, sunbaked island with a population of a few hundred. 'Donald Trump made his money in Manhattan, didn't he?' an Indonesian friend joked when we visited the island, the day before the election. 'If he wins maybe he will build a tower in Run, to say thank you for Manhattan.'

For many decades, Run, and the other spice-growing islands of the Moluccas, provided the Dutch East India Company with huge and easy profits. But then, as European tastes changed, the price of spices began to fall. Drastic measures, like the uprooting of millions of trees and the destruction of warehoused supplies, failed to prevent the company's collapse in the late 18th century.

By the mid-19th century, clove and nutmeg trees were being grown far beyond their original habitat, and the long history of the Spice Islands, as creators of great wealth, had come to an end.

The obvious lesson of this history is that it is impossible to imagine a world without global connections: They have always existed, and no place has escaped their formative influence. But this does not mean that there is any inherent merit in interconnectedness, which has always been accompanied by violence, deepening inequalities and the large-scale destruction of communities. Nor should proponents of unfettered globalization forget that in the 19th century 'free trade' was invoked by Britain and other Western powers to prevent China from stopping the inflow of opium into the country, where it was causing widespread addiction.

These aspects of globalization are often overlooked because the advocacy of interconnectedness has come to be equated with tolerance, while the resistance to it is identified with prejudice. But neither cosmopolitanism nor parochialism is a virtue in itself. We need to ask: cosmopolitanism in the service of what? Protectionism to what end?

The story of the Spice Islands holds another alarming portent. In a clove garden on the island of Ternate, I found that most of the trees were leafless, their trunks the colour of ash. I was told that clove trees are dying all over the island, and the farmers cited the same cause: The trees had been affected by changes in rainfall patterns over the last several years. There was less rain, and it fell more erratically. This, in turn, had led to the spread of blights and disease. The island has also experienced forest fires of unprecedented intensity.

If these changes continue, the clove, one of the earliest of commodities, could be endangered in its ancestral home by greenhouse gas emissions caused precisely by humanity's ever-expanding appetite for commodities.

Only in this one respect are we truly in a new era of interconnectedness.

Contributors

CARLOS DRUMMOND DE ANDRADE (1902-1987) was a Brazilian poet, whose poem - *Canção Amiga* — was on the 50 cruzado novo bill.

AMITAV GHOSH is an award-winning novelist, whose most beloved novels include *The Shadow Lines*, *The Glass Palace*, *The Hungry Tide* and the *Ibis* trilogy. His most recent book is *The Great Derangement: Climate Change and the Unthinkable*.

GHASSAN HAGE is professor of anthropology and social theory at the university of Melbourne, Australia. He has held many visiting professorships around the world including at the American University of Beirut, L'Ecole des Hautes Etudes en Sciences Sociales, Paris, University of Copenhagen, University of Amsterdam and Harvard. His work includes *White Nation* (2000), *Against Paranoid Nationalism* (2003) and *Alter-Politics* (2015).

JOHN BELLAMY FOSTER is Professor of Sociology at the University of Oregon and editor of *Monthly Review* (New York). His most recent books are *The Endless*

Crisis (with Robert W. McChesney, New York: Monthly Review Press, 2012) and *Marx and the Earth* (with Paul Burkett, Chicago: Haymarket, 2017).

MASTURAH ALATAS is the author of a tale about climate change, *The Girl Who Made It Snow in Singapore* (Ethos Books, 2008) and *The Life in the Writing* (Marshall Cavendish, 2010), a memoir-biography of Malaysian sociologist, Syed Hussein Alatas, who was also her father. Born in Singapore, she worked as a journalist in Malaysia before moving to Italy in 1992 where she teaches English at the Univerity of Macerata. A regular contributor to *Counterpunch*, Masturah has completed a novel and is working on another.

NAOMI KLEIN is a Canadian author and journalist who authored three landmark books — *No Logo* (1999), *Shock Doctrine: The Rise of Disaster Capitalism* (2007) and *This Changes Everything: Capitalism vs. The Climate* (2014), which Amitav Ghosh called 'one of the most important books of the decade'. In 2016, Naomi won the Sydney Peace Prize for her work on climate change. Her book *Fences and Windows* was published by LeftWord Books in 2002.

RAFIA ZAKARIA is a columnist for *Dawn* (Pakistan) and the *Boston Review*'s 'Reading Other Women' Series. She is the author of *The Upstairs Wife: An*

Intimate History of Pakistan (Beacon Press) and *Veil* (Bloomsbury). She has written for *The New York Times*, *The Guardian*, *The New Republic*, *The Nation*, *Guernica* and various other publications.

SHALINI SINGH is a Delhi-based journalist, who currently writes for *The Week* and earlier wrote for the *Hindustan Times*. In 2012 she won the Prem Bhatia Award for excellence in environmental reporting. Shalini is a founding trustee at the People's Archive of Rural India (ruralindiaonline.org). In 2013, she was described by *Elle* as 'a headliner, one of journalism's new guard that asks difficult questions, risks life and limb, and will stop at nothing for the truth.'

SUSAN ABULHAWA is a Palestinian novelist and poet. Her most recent novel, *The Blue Between Sky and Water* (Bloomsbury, 2015), is an international best seller, translated into 28 languages. She is also the founder of Playgrounds for Palestine, a volunteer organization dedicated to upholding the Right to Play.

VIJAY PRASHAD is the Chief Editor of LeftWord Books. His most recent book is *The Death of the Nation and the Future of the Arab Revolution* (2016).